PONY

the annual!

2007

What's in PONY the annual!

Fab foals page 90

Treasure hunting Jorja! page 94

Top cross cou tips to try pag

Duggie and Colonel's intruder adventure page 16

Beautiful Arabians page 22

Fess ups! page 58

fun starts here!

Oh Charlie! page 50

Reader's real-life experience page 31

NO MORE HANGING AROUND... TURN THE PAGE AND GET READING!

Pony Watch

How well do you really understand ponies? Most of the ways in which they think and act are down to how they have evolved over hundreds of thousands of years. Here's what makes them tick...

Playing or fighting?!
What he's doing...

It is fascinating watching ponies out in a field together nudging each other, chasing around, perhaps pinching each other a bit. Watch out if it gets a bit more frenzied, with wild chases round the field, and bucking, kicking and lashing out with the front legs. Boisterous play can go a bit beyond a joke...

Legs...
● **Stamping a leg** – if he's not trying to get rid of a fly, it could signal pain
● **Pawing the gound** – preparing to roll or lie down, or showing he's in pain
● **Hindleg waving in the air** – either warning that he's going to kick or is thinking about it!

What he's saying...

As long as things don't get out of hand (or hoof!), this is all part of being a sociable, independently-minded pony. Ponies like to have a companion or two with them – they are herd animals and very sociable. Although they can play on their own, they are much happier in a natural environment where they can play social games. It's a bit like you and your mates: it's good fun to lark around. Falling out a bit is all part of this, though, if there is particularly aggressive behaviour from one individual, you may need to move him away from that group to avoid injury.

Ears...

● **Pricked sharply forwards** – alert, interested or alarmed
● **Clamped back** – cross, possibly aggressive or in pain
● **Sideways** – relaxed, listening or not feeling too good

On the move (and always eating!)
What he's doing...

Do you ever get the feeling that horses and ponies never stop eating? It seems like they're being incredibly greedy, as they spend so much of their time, mouth down, filling their stomachs.

What he's saying...

Wild horses spend most of their time grazing and walking slowly – often covering long distances, and it is completely natural for ponies to eat small amounts of low-concentrated food throughout the day. The digestive system of horses and ponies is designed for this, and, if they get too much in one go, their small stomachs find it hard to cope. This can cause all sorts of digestive problems, some of them really serious. So it is important that we mimic the natural way for horses to eat in the way we keep them: if they are stabled, they need to be fed small amounts of low concentrate food frequently (three times a day), and have plenty of hay to nibble at. If they are kept in a field, they can chomp on the grass, and have a little feed added if necessary – but watch out during seasons when the grass grows quickly, as this can cause serious health problems.

Lying down
What he's doing...

Horses rest during the day as well as at night, and, if relaxed, will lie down in the field or stable. Rest is important for their wellbeing.

What he's saying...

Horses and ponies do need to feel very relaxed and safe to lie down, as they are naturally 'flight' animals (which means that they are always prepared to flee predators). If they are lying down, they won't be so quick off the mark when danger arrives. In a herd, you won't see all members lying down at the same time, as it is important that some of them keep an eye out for danger and can warn the others. However, domestic horses or ponies will sometimes lie down together in a small group if they are in a field they feel particularly secure in.

Sweet dreams
What he's doing...

He lies down with his front legs stretched out and his head and neck on the ground. You see movements in the legs, eyes and ears – and hope that there's nothing wrong with him!

What he's saying...

He's probably in the middle of a deep sleep known as REM, which is a really good, relaxing form of rest. He may be enjoying a good dream. Foals need more restful sleep than adults, but it is important, too, for all ponies' physical and mental well-being to enjoy restful sleep.

Nostrils...
● Flared and open – great interest, fear or excitement
● Semi-open – calm attitude or boredom
● Drawn up and back, wrinkled at the tops – aggression, pain, distress or frustration

Tail...
● Held high – alarm or great interest
● Held high and swaying from side to side – happy, feeling good
● Clamped down – aggression, pain or submission
● Swishing – cross or in distress
● Relaxed – so is the horse!

Drink up!
What he's doing...

When ponies drink, they lower their head to the water's surface and suck the water through the small gap in their lips. It's a very calm, quiet process.

What he's saying...

Water is very, very important, and how much water ponies drink depends on the weather, exercise and water content in the food. Always make sure that your water buckets and water troughs are kept clean so that your pony has access to clean, fresh drinking water throughout the day and night.

Eyes...
● Wide open, whites showing – anxious, frightened
● Slightly closed – dozing off, relaxed
● Soft look – friendly, relaxed
● Sunken eyes with dull appearance – illness or pain

Scratch, scratch!
What he's doing...

Two ponies, standing beside each other, facing each other's tails – nibbling away at the other pony's withers or crest or down the back. We all go 'aah!' but what's going on here?

What he's saying...

Ponies like to groom each other – it's partly friendly and partly practical as it helps get to those itchy spots that are hard to reach. It's a good way for ponies to get to know each other, to build up a friendship and have a good scratch. It can be just as enjoyable for them when a human does it, and you'll know where your pony wants to be rubbed as he moves under your hand or points with his muzzle to an itchy place. When you've got the right spot, he'll raise his muzzle and twitch his top lips with half closed eyes. Pure pleasure!

2006 – the best bits!

Here we take a look back at some of the most memorable events of 2006. We remember record-breaking show jumpers, phenomenal eventing success on the world's stage, and the horse and rider who dared to win show jumping's toughest competition.

William's Derby victory!

The Hickstead Derby is one of the toughest show jumping competitions in the world. The course is high and wide, the famous Derby bank is steep and daunting, and the legendary Devil's Dyke combination is tricky, to say the very least. Only the top riders in the world attempt this course, and only truly great horses will win the title.

In 2006, there were no clears in the first round of the Derby competition but Geoff Billington, William Funnell and David McPherson all completed the course on four faults and went forward to a jump-off. It was a nail-biting end to an intense competition. David McPherson was first up, and he and Bob's Diamond knocked one rail down. Geoff Billington and Cassabachus went for it and produced a fast round but, with two fences down, the competition was in Willam's hands.

As William and Cortaflex Mondriaan set off, you could feel the crowd willing the pair to clear the course. William took his time and kept the enormous Mondriaan under control so that he produced a brilliant clear round to take the title. It was a truly magical moment as the big bay touched down after the final fence and William knew that, at last, the title was his!

As he completed his lap of honour, there was no wider grin than that on William's face; it was the perfect end to a truly incredible competition.

William and Cortaflex Mondriaan, 2006 Derby winners!

Andrew Hoy and Moonfleet led from the start!

Andrew's long-awaited Badminton win!

Badminton is the crème de la crème of four-star eventing. The combination of dressage, cross-country and showjumping is second to none, and riders flock to the beautiful grounds from all over the world for a chance to win the title.

In 2006 Badminton was all about one man, Andrew Hoy, who led from the dressage phase. Andrew first tackled the event in 1979, but it has taken until now for him to take the title. Andrew completed on his dressage score, a feat only achieved by two riders this year, jumping clear over the long, tough, cross-country course and the technical show jumping track.

Andrew's Badminton success followed his brilliant win in Kentucky, giving him the chance of winning the Rolex Grand Slam, which was last won by Pippa Funnell in 2003. He needed to win Burghley but, in a nail-biting finish, he came second to fellow Australian Lucinda Fredericks.

Photo courtesy of the British Open Show jumping Championships 2006

The 7'3" Puissance wall!

Record breakers!

This year's British Open Show jumping Championships saw its puissance record broken not once, not twice, but three times! Five horses made the fifth round of the competition to tackle the 7ft 3in puissance wall. First to go was John Whitaker and Lactic Two. The talented grey slithered up and over the wall, leaving it standing and setting a new event record.

Next up was John's son Robert Whitaker, whose horse Finbarr V just knocked a brick from the great wall. Ben Maher and Eperian Du Fouquet were in the same boat as Robert, narrowly missing the target.

John Whitaker's second ride, Exploit Du Roulard, cleared the wall with inches to spare in his best jump of the competition, equalling Lactic's record. Last to go was Robert Maguire with Mr Cawley, in their second puissance competition together. The chestnut boldly leaped over the fence and became the third horse to jump the 7ft 3in wall!

Zara Phillips winning the World Eventing Championships in Aachen!

European and World Champion, Zara Phillips!

When Zara Phillips and Toytown stepped out onto the international arena at Aachen, sceptics thought the pair didn't have enough mileage under their belts since the European Championships to stand a chance at the World Championships – what did they know?

Zara and Toytown rescued British team hopes with their inspiring dressage test, which earned them a score of 41.7 penalties. On day two of the three-day event, Zara and Toytown produced one of just 11 clear rounds across country which were inside the time limit. It was not a straightforward round, with trouble at the first water fence and a heart-stopping moment when Toytown banked the brush fence. However, Zara sat tight and Toytown found that extra leg when he most needed it, and together their determination and talent got them round.

When Zara entered the arena for the final phase, the show jumping, she had a fence in hand over silver medallist Clayton Fredericks. Toytown is known for being a difficult horse to ride in the show jumping, but Zara kept her cool and they jumped a brilliant round with just one fence down and one time penalty. Zara said of her horse, Toytown, "He jumped fantastically and tried his heart out." Zara said that she really wanted to win a medal for her close friend, Sherelle Duke, who tragically died in an eventing accident a week before the event.

To win the European Championships was an amazing achievement in itself, but to go on to hold the World Championship title at the same time makes Zara Phillips a true eventing hero. She and Toytown are an incredible combination, and one which we hope to see much more of in future.

WHO AM I?

Our eight mystery breeds have each given you three clues to help you guess who they are. Use your detective skills and pony knowledge to try and identify all the breeds. When you've finished, turn to page 98 to check your answers!

● I am an endangered species, with only about 140 of my kind living wild in our native breeding area.
● I'm known for my distinctive mealy muzzle.
● I am native to the British Isles.

WHO AM I? _____

● I have up to five gaits!
● The country I come from is a very cold.
● I am always referred to as a horse, even though I'm always under 14.2hh.

WHO AM I? _____

● I'm a close relation to the horse.
● I come from France.
● I'm well-known for my height and my curly coat.

WHO AM I? _____

● I am usually roan in colour.
● An anagram of my name is DARN SEA IN.
● My homeland is both France and Belgium.

WHO AM I? _____

- I'm believed to have pre-historic origins.
- I have a two-layered winter coat which protects me from the cold, wet, winters of my native country.
- Many of my breed have eel stripes or zebra markings.

WHO AM I? _____

- I was nearly wiped out during the Second World War when my native grazing area was used by the military for training.
- I can be up to 12.2hh high.
- Between the 12th and 15th century, I was used to haul tin from tin mines.

WHO AM I? _____

- When I'm standing up in-hand, I'm said to resemble an H.
- I'm originally from England, but am now popular in Holland and the USA.
- I just love to trot, and am most commonly used for harness work.

WHO AM I? _____

- I'm named after the English county I originate from.
- I'm always chesnut in colour.
- I'm traditionally used for ploughing and other heavy work.

WHO AM I?

_____

HOW DID YOU DO?

1-3
We hate to say it, but you're really not much of a detective, are you? Flick through your old copies of PONY Magazine and swat up on horse and pony breeds, so that next time you don't have any trouble identifying a pony!

4-6
Well done! It's not easy to know everything about every breed when there are so many gorgeous horses and ponies to learn about!

OVER 6
Top marks for you, detective! It seems like you aren't going to let anyone fool you – well done!

Why we love CONNEMARAS

You could say that PONY Magazine is biased, but we think that the Connemara is one of the best breeds of pony around. Here's why...

Delectable Duggie

When the gorgeous Duggie, a pure-bred Connemara, stepped off the horsebox and waltzed into the PONY office a year ago, we knew we had someone special on our team! We'd been told that he was handsome, brave and an ace jumper, and we soon found out that he has more character than most humans. He took one look at us, decided we were OK, put his head down to eat – and we all fell in love.

Duggie arrives at the office!

So why's Duggie so special?

Like most Connemaras, Duggie is a real looker. He has large, kind eyes, and pert ears. He's strong and compact, with sloping shoulders and good, sturdy legs. His hindquarters are muscular and strong and he has strong hooves. He's rugged without being macho. But it's not just his physical characteristics that make him special, it's that magical 'presence' which Connemaras have that set them apart. There's a kind of 'look at me' quality that just makes you want to stop and stare!

Duggie's friend Soloman

Fun to be with

You'll never find a Connemara boring to be with. They ooze personality and are highly intelligent. Don't be fooled by their dreamy eyes: If you don't handle them properly or treat them well, they'll let you know. But, if you do, they are incredibly kind, gentle and genuine, and will reward you with loyalty and affection. They are very sensible, even when you take them to exciting places like shows, and are brilliant as Pony Club ponies. And they learn things quickly – you don't have to explain what to do too often as they just get it right away.

Duggie and his fan club!

Brilliant at jumping

If you like jumping, you'll love jumping a Connemara. They are very sure-footed, with good knee and hock action, which means that they are brilliant at jumping. This photo of Kiltartan Easter Prince (aka Boy) shows how much he enjoys jumping – his ears are pricked, he's really alert and he's picking up his front feet neatly to clear the jump.

Connemaras may not be terribly big or tall, but they have a huge jump in them. And, because they are so calm, they will tackle most things, whether cross-country, show jumping, out hacking or hunting.

Connemaras love to jump!

Ireland's best

Lots of great things come from Ireland, but the best must be the Connemara which is Ireland's only native breed of pony.

● The Connemara is said by some to date back 2,500 years when Celtic warriors brought their dun ponies to the island to pull chariots and carts. But there's also another story about how they came to be in Ireland: legend has it that, in 1588, some horses from the Spanish Armada wrecked off the coast of Ireland swam ashore and mated with local ponies.

● **There's evidence that Spanish stallions were imported to Ireland from the 14th to 17th century – and if you look at a typical Connemara, you can see a similarity with those beautiful Andalucians from Spain.**

● The Connemara emerged as a sure-footed mountain and moorland pony which thrived in these rocky coastal areas on sparse rations.

● **As farmers started to tame these wild ponies, they found they were good at pulling laden carts, carrying heavy loads filled with peat or seaweed on their backs, and, on Sundays, transporting the farmer and his family to Mass. The combination of a kind nature and strong body made the Connemara indispensable to these people.**

All colours

You often see grey Connemaras, but did you know you can get black, bay, brown (in fact, any solid colour) Connemaras too?! When Duggie was joined in the PONY office by Soloman this year, we saw how gorgeous they are in bay. Dun is a common colour, and you can see them sometimes in palomino and dark-eyed cream.

The perfect family pony

Because they are so sturdy, Connemaras are ideal for all the family. Lightweight adults can ride them, so, if you don't mind sharing, you may find that Mum or Dad will be begging you for a ride on your Connemara.

Dug and Sol out riding

Did you know?

● Seaweed forms part of the diet of those Connemaras living naturally, near the seashore in western Ireland.

● Pure-bred Connemaras can be anything between 133cms (12.2hh) and 148cms (14.2hh) in height.

● Their thick tails are like a rug against the wind and rain – just watch a Connemara turn its back against the weather, and lower its head when everything is wet and horrid!

More info

Contact the British Connemara Pony Society, East Green, Bowsden, Berwick upon Tweed, Northumberland TD15 2TJ. Tel: 01289 388800.
www.britishconnemaras.co.uk

Duggie's do's & don'ts

● **Do** treat us as intelligent beings – we were blessed with big brains
● **Don't over-face us – we'll do everything we can to please you, which could land us both in trouble!**
● **Do** keep us busy, as we are inquisitive souls and like to be kept occupied.

Colonel's Cunning Plan...

With the family away for the day, the ponies think they're in for a quiet time. But they're wrong...

PART 1

Suddenly, a stranger went past the field.

Oh, you gave me quite a turn. Who are you?

The person crept towards the stable yard.

How rude. I'm sure he's up to no good – and everyone's out for the day!

Perhaps we should let him take it, it would save us having to carry everyone around the countryside. Show him where the key is kept...

Er, I like the way you think, but it's a bit of a cheek, isn't it. I mean, stealing stuff that isn't yours?

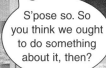

S'pose so. So you think we ought to do something about it, then?

Colonel, do you think you can wriggle under the fence?

Well, if I could, you wouldn't see me for dust, would you?

Well, *I* know who to call! Leave it to me. I have a cunning plan to fox that burglar!

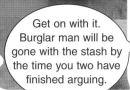

Yeah, great idea. Got a mobile on you? We'll give Sherlock Holmes and Miss Marple a call.

Get on with it. Burglar man will be gone with the stash by the time you two have finished arguing.

Who will Colonel call to help? Will the burglar get away? Will Duggie and Soloman ever stop being sarcastic? Find out in part two of *Colonel's Cunning Plan!*

Turn to page 78!

Quick Quiz

1 Have you put together a checklist of the type of pony that would suit you?
Yes ☐   No ☐

2 Have you thought about how you will manage your time so that you can devote lots of time to care for your pony?
Yes ☐   No ☐

3 Lots of things can go wrong with ponies. Do you know what the most common forms of illness are and what you can do about them?
Yes ☐   No ☐

4 The cost of buying the pony is only the beginning of lots and lots of costs that come with pony ownership. Can you write down a list of at least five things you would need to pay for from time to time, and five things you would need to pay for regularly?
Yes ☐   No ☐

5 Do you know the main things to look for in providing a safe, comfortable, warm stable?
Yes ☐   No ☐

6 Have you thought about turn-out and do you know what to check for to make sure the field is safe for ponies?
Yes ☐   No ☐

7 Will either of your parents – or another responsible adult – be involved in caring for your pony with you?
Yes ☐   No ☐

8 Do you know the basic principles of feeding horses and ponies?
Yes ☐   No ☐

9 Can you put on a saddle, bridle, headcollar, rugs and other tack and equipment you will be using?
Yes ☐   No ☐

10 Do you understand the importance of getting a vet to 'vet' a pony you are seriously considering buying?
Yes ☐   No ☐

Now read the feature to discover whether you ticked the right boxes! You'll soon see whether you're ready to own your own pony!

Are you ready... ... to own a pony?

Size: it's important!

1 Before you embark on your pony-buying project, think hard about exactly what type of pony you are looking for. What do you want to do with him – are you going to compete, or are you happy to hack out? What size would work best for you? Will anyone else (maybe a parent) be riding him, in which case you will need a pony that can take their weight, too. Think about age and temperament, how much you can afford and whether you particularly want a gelding or a mare. If colour is important, then put this on the list, too!

If you're mad about ponies, and you don't own your own, the chances are that there is only one thing on your mind – owning a pony! You can't understand why Mum and Dad tell you that it's too much of a commitment, or costs too much, or you don't have the time for it, or a zillion-and-one other reasons why you can't get one (funny how they're so good at dreaming up excuses!). But maybe they're right – it is a massive responsibility. Before you even think of taking that big leap, check out our quick quiz to see whether you really are ready. You have to be really truthful with your answers!

2 We all lead busy lives these days, and fitting in the constant care involved in owning a pony really eats into our time. You need to consider how you'll feel going out early in the mornings when it's pouring with rain, and to be sure that you understand that the commitment to your pony means that, even when you're feeling tired, or have loads of homework to do, you need to fit this around your number one responsibility. If you have any doubts about your ability to give your new pony 'your all', don't do it – wait until you are able to before taking on this responsibility. This is not something you can do light-heartedly.

3 The most common problems that vets see are colic, lameness, laminitis, respiratory (breathing) difficulties, sweet itch and skin conditions like mud fever. But there are also loads and loads of things that can go wrong with ponies. Whilst you can't guarantee your pony will stay well, there's no doubt that good care and management will prevent most things from going wrong. And the only way to be sure of providing good care is to learn lots and lots about horse management. So, if you don't know much about these, and other, health issues, you need to find out about them.

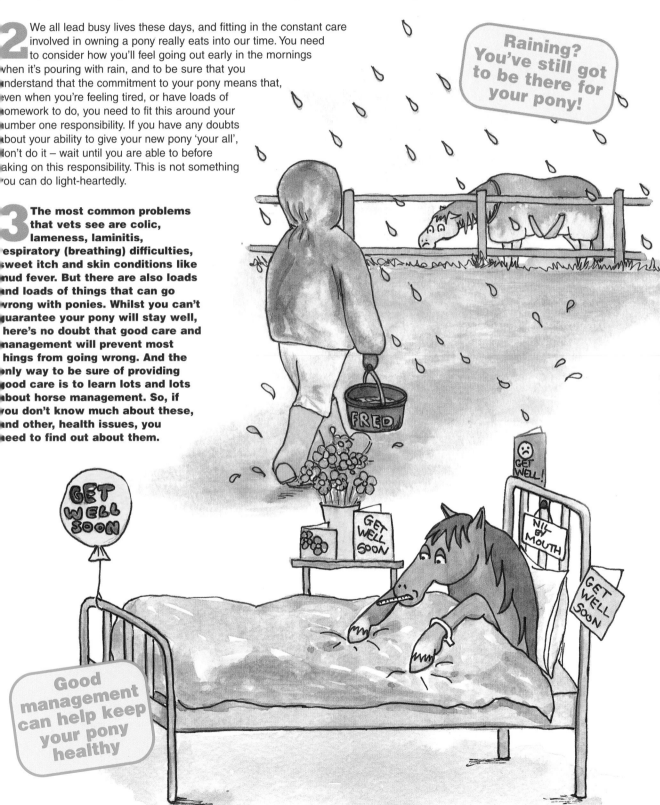

Raining? You've still got to be there for your pony!

Good management can help keep your pony healthy

19

6 Being out in a field with friends is natural to ponies, and they are much happier and healthier if you plan the turn-out facilities carefully. But make sure that the field is fenced safely and has a good field shelter (this is particularly important if there are no big trees in the field which could provide natural shelter). Dig up poisonous plants such as ragwort. Put a padlock on the gate to deter thieves. And make sure there is clean, fresh water in the water trough at all times (it will need cleaning out regularly, more often in the summer).

4 Five things you will need to pay for regularly are:
- **Shoeing and/or trimming (every six weeks)**
- **Worming medicines (about every six weeks)**
- **Feed and hay (as often as it is eaten!). Feed supplements if needed**
- **Livery fees if you keep the pony at a riding centre or livery yard**
- **Bedding if you keep the pony at home.**

Five things you will need to buy from time to time:
- Tack and equipment, plus repairs
- Insurance to cover things like vets' fees, or, if you don't have insurance, then you will need to know that you can afford the cost of veterinary treatment if necessary – this can be very expensive if there is a serious problem
- Dental care and vaccinations such as for tetanus and 'flu.
- Tack cleaner and conditioner, medical lotions and potions when needed
- Repairs to fencing and stabling if your pony is kept at home.

If you add to these your own riding gear plus lessons (which you will need whether or not you own a pony), and are aware that there are likely to be other costs we haven't listed here, you'll get the idea – owning a pony is mega expensive.

7 However much you know about ponies, and however devoted you are to them, it is a real plus if you know someone horsy who lives close by, or if your parents are horsy. You can ask their advice if you are worried about something, and they could (if you are really nice to them!) provide you with back up if you are away somewhere.

5 Your pony deserves a safe, warm home – so check that the stable is, firstly, large enough for him. The minimum size for a small pony is three metres by three metres, but for most ponies it should be no smaller than three metres by three-and-a-half metres. There should be no sharp objects sticking out of the wall (eg nails) and the stable needs to be clean and well-ventilated so that the air stays fresh. You will need to put enough bedding on the floor so that your pony doesn't scrape himself on the hard concrete when he gets up from a nap! (Or you could look into rubber matting to be fitted to the stable floor.)

8 You need to know how to put on a headcollar, saddle, bridle and rugs properly – partly for safety reasons and partly because, if you don't know what you are doing, you will irritate your pony. (It's a bit like someone helping you pull on your swimming goggles – you know how annoying it is if they pull your hair or pinch your skin.)

If you don't know how to put tack and equipment on, you will either need an experienced adult looking after your pony with you, or you should livery him at a riding school where experienced instructors can show you what to do.

Oh dear – a bit more homework needed!

9 ● Feed little and often – horses' digestive systems are designed to receive small amounts of high fibre feed frequently. Feeding too much at one time will cause your pony problems
● Make sure that your pony has clean, fresh water all the time
● Feed the right balance of feeds for the type, temperament and age of pony and the work he is doing
● Make any changes to his diet very gradually so his digestive system has time to get used to them
● Do not exercise straight after feeding – allow at least an hour before riding your pony
● Feed plenty of roughage
● Keep to the same feed times each day.

10 OK – you have found the pony of your dreams! But how do you know that he is sound and in good health? Get him vetted by a horse vet who will check out the most obvious signs of ill health and lameness. A 'vetting' is essential if you want to take out insurance, but, even if you do not, it is foolish not to have your pony vetted. If you can afford it, have the most comprehensive vetting you can. The money will be well spent and will either put your mind at rest or warn you away from a pony that could turn out to have problems which could cause both of you lots of distress, plus the agony of big vet's bills.

A vetting is vital!

artwork: Lisa Butler

It's pretty obvious that there is masses to think about if you are really serious about owning a pony. Believe it or not, we've only scratched the surface in this feature. If you really love horses and ponies, you will make sure you learn as much as you can about how to care for them and ride them before you take this big step. If you do, you will hopefully have many happy years with your favourite, four-legged friend!

The Arabian

History

Records of Arabian horses go back to 3,000 BC. The Arabian came to be prized by the Bedouin tribes for its unique characteristics. The mares were used in tribal warfare because stallions were more likely to neigh, alerting the enemy. The mares and foals lived in camps, often sharing their owner's tent, and the children played with the foals – so the horses and humans became very close to each other. Its long association with man has meant that the Arabian forms strong attachments to humans, even to this day.

The Arabian was much-admired and those with power and wealth built up collections of them. It became a status symbol to own the finest horses.

The tail is set on high and, when the horse is moving, is carried high – particularly when the horse is moving fast or is excited. The tail (and mane) is long, fine and silky

The back is quite short and strong

The coat is fine and silky

Conformation

What makes them so special?

Arabians look beautiful, with their exquisite head and large eyes. They are very strong and fast and are considered to be so perfect that humans can improve on them – that is why Arabians in the GB are never trimmed. Their manes and tails are left long and flowing, their whiskers kept intact. But they are not 'just a pretty face'! The harsh desert conditions they lived in ensured that only the fittest survived.

'Drinking the wind'

No, this is not the name of the latest dance craze! The beautiful way in which Arabians hold their heads high, with nostrils flared wide, is known as 'drinking the wind'. It is thought to keep the Arabian's head above the dust of the desert, helping him to breathe.

The neck is long and the throat graceful

The head is one of the most striking features. It is very refined, with great width across the forehead tapering to a fine muzzle. A 'dish' below the eye is quite common and the ears, which are very fine, often have inward-curving tips

The hooves are strong and circular

Arabians are good at...

...virtually anything that demands speed, stamina and courage. That's why there are so many top long-distance Arabians! They are also great for people who are loyal to them and who respect them – they give great loyalty and love in return.

Did you know?

● Arabians come in a variety of gorgeous colours – grey, chestnut, bay, brown and – very rarely – black.
● Though there is no height limit, Arabians are usually between 14.2hh and 15.2hh.
● Most horses have 18 ribs, but the Arabian has 17!
● Arabians have only 16 tail bones compared with other horses which have 18!

Big influence

As an old, pure breed the Arabian has influenced virtually every other breed of horse around today. There is hardly a breed of light horse that does not have some Arab blood in it.
● Every Thoroughbred alive today can be traced back in the male line to three phenomenal Arabian stallions – the Darley Arabian, the Godolphin Arabian and the Byerley Turk.
● The beautiful Lipizzaner contains much Arabian blood.
● Native pony breeds show degrees of Arabian blood in them – the Welsh Mountain Pony in particular has been clearly influenced by this remarkable and beautiful breed.

More info

Contact the Arab Horse Society of Great Britain, Windsor House, Ramsbury, Marlborough, Wiltshire SN8 2PE. Tel: 01672 521411.
www.arabhorsesociety.org

I love Sally

by PONY reader Alice Child

I was out in the field, dozing with my mates Bailey and Sherbert. It was warm, and I was casually flicking the annoying buzzies with my tail. Sally was late. I didn't mind really, I preferred being with Bailey and Sherbert than going to a carry. Well, coloured bouncing is OK, as long as there are no ditches for monsters to hide in, and so is brown bouncing, but I hate bending carries. In those, there aren't any bounces, coloured or brown.

> *I then noticed a little girl, much smaller than Sally, standing down at the bottom of the field watching us*

Suddenly, the sound of a swinging gate broke into my thoughts, and there was Sally, my human, calling me. I trotted up to her and – as gently as I could – nudged her. I loved Sally. She was my best friend and I was her's. There was nothing I wouldn't do for Sally, well almost nothing. I didn't like going into the noisy rattling box on wheels… it wants to eat me, but no pony I know likes going in them.

Sally put on my ropes and slipped an apple into my mouth. Sally knew I loved apples. I didn't mind leaving Sherbert and Bailey when I had Sally with me. I then noticed a little girl, much smaller than Sally, standing down at the bottom of the field watching us. I didn't like the look of her; she had chestnut hair and Sherbert says that chestnut human girls are lively and noisy. As we walked past her, Sally gave her a little smile and said something I didn't understand. I don't understand a lot of human talking. I have only learnt the important things like *food* and *parties*. I love going to parties. I always know when we are going to one when Sally comes very early in the morning. At parties, we sometimes do bending and brown bouncing, but we mostly do coloured bouncing and something called showing. Showing is okay, I like being cleaned and brushed until I shine, but after that it gets boring. All that walking round in circles without doing any bounces.

Sally and I got to my house and she undid my ropes and went to get the carrying equipment. It's not my fault we need to use them. Once, Sally tried to have a carry without the tight-belt mechanism and I decided to test her, to see if she could still ride me OK. I only gave a tiny buck but she slid off. She's never tried it since.

I realised I had a new bed. That wouldn't do! I kicked the woodchips off the sides. I rolled, so woodchips flew everywhere, then I got up and knocked my water bucket over. I looked at my masterpiece – something was missing. I did a big poo in the middle of the house. Now it was just like it was before, *perfect*. Looking out through my front window, I saw Sally coming back. She laughed when she saw so many woodchips in my mane. Then she sighed when she saw my bed. But she wasn't really mad, this is what we do. We are never angry at each other, because we are *best friends*.

Sally placed the tight-belt mechanism on my back and tried to fasten it. Well, she didn't get very far. I blew out my tummy so it was harder for her. Humans are quite silly – no matter how many times I do this, Sally never works it out. Then she came to my head with the metal stick-steering device. I opened my mouth for her. I don't like doing it, but I did it for my Sally. She quickly got the foot cleaner and scraped my hooves clean. As she passed me, I nipped her bottom, just to show her I was boss. You have to do this with humans. I led Sally out of the house and she lifted herself onto my back before we trotted into the square school, which is where I give Sally her lessons.

As I was warming up Sally, I noticed the little girl again. She was standing with her mum by the gate, watching us. Sally shifted me into a trot. She felt tense, I didn't know why. I tried to relax her by bending my neck but I could tell it didn't help. I was confused. What did Sally want? We moved into a canter and she began to relax when she turned towards the bounce in the middle of the school. I sped up, but again, she tensed. I flew over the bounce, but because of her hesitation, I

> *Recently, when I've been carrying Sally, it's got a lot harder for me*

knocked it with my back leg, and the pole fell. We never did that, we're a great team! We turned to do it again, and this time, she didn't pull me back so we sailed over it and cleared it easily. I decided Sally must be tired.

Sally wasn't the only one who got tired. Recently, when I've been carrying Sally, it's got a lot harder for me. When doing bounces, getting off the ground is more difficult. Sally wants to do bigger bounces, too. I normally wouldn't mind, but Sally seems so heavy these days. I told Sherbert this. She is four years older than me, so I thought she could help, but she didn't. She just looked sad and cantered off. Mares!

> *The girl nudged me lightly again, and I cantered*

Posed by models

Then, Sally walked me over to the little girl and got off. The little girl put on her hard hat, her hand warmers and her armour. Sally never wore her armour at home, only when we do brown bounces. Then, guess what the little girl did? She got on me! I didn't like it! The little girl kicked me to go on. She didn't kick as hard as Sally so I decided I wouldn't move. The little girl kicked a bit harder and still I didn't move. I looked at Sally; why wasn't I carrying her? But then, Sally whispered in my ear, "*Be good*." I didn't want to be good for the little girl, so instead, I was good for Sally. I walked forward perfectly, bending the whole time. The little girl nudged me with her feet and I trotted. The whole time, Sally was watching. The girl nudged me lightly again, and I cantered. We turned towards the bounce and I began to enjoy myself. I flew over the jump, just like I do with Sally. The girl wasn't as good as Sally at bouncing, but she was much lighter so I could easily do the bigger jump that the girl's mum put up. When the girl got off, she gave me a big pat and so did her mum. I decided she wasn't lively or noisy. I was about to nuzzle her, when I remembered Sally. How could I have wanted to nuzzle her? I only loved Sally.

> *I thought I'd make Sally feel better by nudging and loving her, but I made it worse. She began crying*

fast gallop. There was a sideways tree that didn't look normal. Trees are meant to go up. Sally cantered me towards it! I stopped in front of the scary thing. I wanted to run away, but I didn't because I could trust Sally. I realised it was a bounce! I jumped it from a standstill, because I knew that's what Sally wanted. Sally landed on my neck, which surprised me, but I stood still. Sally patted me and we did it again before galloping home. I loved that hack.

One morning, Sally brought me my party shoes and wrapped them around my legs. We were going to a party! Sally was in a bit of a strange mood, I thought she must be nervous as she often is

horses? I stayed close to Sally. The whole time she was talking to me in a soothing voice. She rubbed me down and took off my party shoes. Then I saw the little girl. She was beginning to get on my nerves, she was following us everywhere. She came over, patted me and smiled at Sally. Sally didn't say anything, but untied me and followed the little girl. This was unusual. Normally, Sally began by putting carrying equipment on, or getting into her smart clothes, or cleaning me.

Sally looked very sad now. I went into a very big, clean house. This was very odd. It smelt clean, as if no horse had ever been there before. I didn't like being in another horse's house. I stayed in one corner munching hay out of a big net. I remembered that Bailey had told me that he had been to an overnight party, he called them sleepovers. At the time, they had sounded fun, but now I wasn't so sure. Then Sally gave me a hug and both she and the girl left. Probably to get her number – she often did this at parties.

I looked around me. I was scared. It was light in this house, and the front window looked outside, but I didn't like it. In the house next to me was a Shetland – skewbald and very pretty. She told me her name was Button, and that Harriet's sister was her human. The black mare opposite me was Clarie, and Harriet's mum was *her* human. I then asked her, "Is this a sleepover?" She looked at me in a sympathetic way which I didn't like. I wanted Sally, where was Sally? Sally came running in and gave me lots of apples and a big hug. She told me she loved me and always would. Then she was gone.

The days passed. I became good friends with Button and Clarie, although Button's snoring was a bit of a nuisance, and Clarie could be quite grumpy. Mares! Harriet was easy to carry, and it was good fun teaching her to bounce. I learned that the yard belonged to Harriet's mum, and all the horses there were members of the family, and so was I. Harriet was Button's old human, but she had grown too big for Button. I realised that this was what had happened with Sally and me. Harriet loved me as much as Sally did. She gave me lots of mints with holes, and carrots. She came to see me every day and cuddled me. And then I realised I had a new best friend.

That night, I was thinking about the girl. Sally had told me the girl was called Harriet. She then cried a bit and told me she loved me. I wanted to tell her too, but I can't talk human. As long as I had Sally, I knew I was safe.

After a few days, the girl came back and we did some brown bouncing. I was good again. I began to like this little girl; she was gentle and nice and gave me carrots. I like carrots, but not as much as apples. Sally gave me apples. The next day, I took Sally on a long outside carry, which she calls hacks. I like hacks. We always go into the big field and have a

before parties. I thought I'd make Sally feel better by nudging and loving her, but I made it worse. She began crying. I made a last attempt at being good by going into the horse-eating box on wheels, even though it had taken me ages to train Sally to expect me only to go in after lots of food... and apples.

> *I asked Button, "Is this a sleepover?" She looked at me in a sympathetic way...*

After the noise, bumpy journey, I led Sally out of the box. It was very quiet, and not like any other party I had ever been to. Where were all the other

One morning, I was grazing in the field when I heard a familiar voice. I looked up – Sally! I cantered towards her and she gave me an apple.

"Oh my boy," said Sally, "you look so small!" That was a cheek, I thought, she looked huge! However did I carry her?

I will never forget Sally; I will always love her.

HORSY HEROES

The equestrian world is filled with many amazing horses, trainers, riders and breeders. Choosing just four Heroes was a painstaking process, but we've done it! The stars we've chosen have been successful beyond your wildest dreams, they're talented and brave, with courage and skills to die for. But, above all, the Heroes we've chosen have formed special relationships with their horses or rider, they've helped others, and they've kept their sense of humour – so let us introduce you to the first PONY *Heroes!*

KING OF THE CROP!

Mary King has had a career lasting over 20 years, she's won countless medals, survived a broken neck and come back for more – and she's done most of it with a huge smile across her face!

Mary started learning to ride after a family day out to Badminton Horse Trials. She's not from a horsy background, so in the early days she would turn her hand to just about anything that would help her pay for her eventing career. In 1985, Mary competed in her first Badminton and came seventh, quite an achievement for a debut performance, and the event has remained her favourite ever since. She went on to win Badminton twice, with King William in 1992 and in 2000 with Star Appeal. Mary's partnership with King William resulted in him being the only event horse to score over 2000 points in competition.

Mary has represented Great Britain in the last four Olympic games. Despite fantastic performances in the first three games, coming 9th, 12th and 7th individually, it wasn't until 2004 that Mary got her coveted Olympic medal when she won a team silver medal in Athens.

Mary has won the title of British Champion a record four times, and has helped win four team gold European and World Championship medals. Mary's determination to succeed has made her the gutsy, hugely talented, rider that she is today. As well as competing to the highest level, Mary has also been hugely successful in breeding a new generation of event horses.

John and Peppermill!

Mary at Badminton!

SHOW JUMPING LEGEND

John Whitaker MBE is a corner post of Britain's most famous show jumping family. His career has lasted over 30 [ye]ars, and he was just 18 years old when he [fir]st partnered Ryan's Son, the horse that [to]ok him into the big time. Ryan's Son was [de]scribed as an odd looking horse, but that [di]dn't stop the pair winning team silver at [th]e Los Angeles Olympic games.

In 1985, John partnered the beautiful grey, [M]ilton. Their strong partnership led to Milton [be]coming the first horse, outside of racing, [to] win over a million pounds before he retired [in] 1994.

John has represented Great Britain in four [Ol]ympic games, five World Championships (winning three team bronze medals and silver team and individual medals), and nine European Championships (picking up 12 medals)!

John has won the Hickstead Derby four times, on four different horses. His Derby win in 1998 with Gammon put the veteran horse in the record books for being the oldest horse to win the title at the age of 21. John has also clocked up three King George V Gold Cup wins – phew!

John's amazing success has shown the depth of the relationships he has with the horses he rides. In a discipline where horses can change hands many times in their careers, John has shown the importance of the bond between horse and rider through the amazing careers of his horses, Ryan's Son, Milton, Gammon, Welham, Lactic and now Peppermill – to name a few.

Primmore's Pride in Athens!

ONE IN A MILLION!

Primmore's Pride is quite simply an eventing legend. Partnered by top rider, Pippa Funnell, Primmore's pride has won almost every eventing title a British rider could wish to! The big bay is not known for being an easy ride, but his talent and relationship with Pippa has led him to become one of the all-time great event horses.

In 2003, Primmore's Pride helped Pippa to win two of the three competitions which made up her Rolex Grand Slam, by winning both Kentucky and Burghley. Two years later, in 2005, he also won Badminton with Pippa – the other event which makes the Grand Slam – proving that he has what it takes to be the best over almost any course.

Primmore's Pride and Pippa were selected to compete in the Athens' Olympic games in 2004. The pair got off to a flying start, performing one of the fabulous dressage tests the gelding has become renowned for. They incurred time penalties across country, as they adjusted to the new short format, and together won the bronze medal individually and helped team GB to the silver medal position. He is quite simply, one of the best!

MASSIVE MEDAL HAUL!

Lee Pearson MBE OBE, started riding as a child when he couldn't keep up with his mates on their BMX bikes. Instead he rode Sally, a donkey who would buck off [ev]eryone but Lee!

Lee started riding in para dressage competitions in 1998. [In] just eight years, he has won 15 gold medals, including [thr]ee at the Sydney Paralympics in 2000, and three at the [20]04 Athens Paralympics.

Lee is also the only disabled rider to win a British [dr]essage National title in able bodied competitions, after he [an]d the dun gelding, Blue Circle Boy, won the Elementary [Re]stricted title in 2003.

Lee's disabilities mean that he is classified as a grade one [rid]er, the most severely disabled category. However, his [ph]enomenal talent and determination have led Lee to [co]mpete in class three competitions, which have a much [hig]her degree of technical difficulty, and also in able bodied [co]mpetition. Lee is a far greater rider than most people could [ev]er hope to be, and is a true inspiration to everyone as he [sh]ows that no obstacle need stand in the way of your goals.

Lee and Blue Circle Boy!

Good Health

Horses and ponies are pretty clever at telling us if they are feeling well or not, even though they can't talk to us in plain English. So don't wait until they actually get ill before you do something about it – learn to read the signs of good health so that you pick up the warning signals when they happen.

Eyes look bright and clear

There should be no redness in the whites of the eyes or any discharges coming out of the eyes. No obvious signs of discomfort such as frequently rubbing or closing the eyes. The mucous membranes (around the eyelids) should be salmon pink in colour.

Nostrils

A slight, watery discharge, particularly after exercise, is not a problem. But there should be no abnormal (yellowy-creamy, thick, sticky) discharges from the nose.

Looking good – check out the eyes and nostrils

Skin...

...should be bright and smooth. Run your hand through the coat – this should feel silky and smooth in unclipped areas. No swellings, sores or dry, scurfy brittleness.

Keep an eye on eating habits

Eating

If a pony with a good appetite suddenly loses it, this is a clear warning that something is wrong. Quidding (food dropping out of the corners of the mouth) shows that the teeth may need a rasp. Be aware of your pony's normal eating habits, and check out changes to these.

Drinking

Water is the most important thing for all horses, more important than food! Horses' bodies have a high level (approximately 60%) of water in them, and will suffer if they become dehydrated. If your fave pony is drinking more or less than usual, get this checked out.

Droppings

It sounds yucky, but have a look at the droppings! They should just break on hitting the ground. If they are very hard or very runny, then something is not quite right. If they smell unusually awful (more than the usual 'pooh' smell), that's not right, either. Check out their colour, too – it shouldn't be too dark or too pale.

Urine

Should be yellowish in colour – not too green or too pale – and should not smell unusually strong.

Breathing

Use a watch with a second hand to measure the breathing rate

This should be silent and smooth. If it is very noisy, or very rapid when the pony isn't moving, then there could be a problem. Horses take about eight to 14 breaths in a minute (in and out counts as one) and you can measure this by watching a pony's flanks and using a watch with a second hand. Stand behind and slightly to one side of the horse, and watch the opposite flank rise and fall.

Pulse

This measures the heart beat and is a good indicator of good or bad health. A very rapid or very slow pulse signals a problem that could be serious. To take the pulse, feel under the jawbone for several seconds as you wait to feel the pulse. Count, using a watch with a second hand. If the pony has been resting, then the pulse can be anything between 32 to 42 beats per minute. By taking your pony's pulse regularly, you will know what his normal pulse is.

Taking a pony's pulse

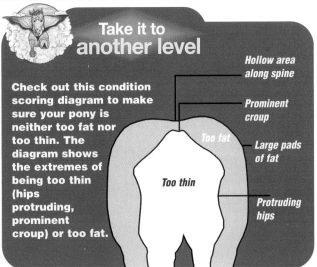

Temperature

It's best to get someone with experience to take the temperature for you. They should use a veterinary thermometer and shake the mercury down with a snapping movement of the wrist to get it below the normal figure. They'll then lubricate the bulb of the thermometer (this is the bit which will go into the horse's rectum) with Vaseline. Standing behind and to the left of the pony, they should pull the dock towards them and insert the thermometer several inches into the rectum, using a gentle, twisting movement. The thermometer should be left in place for 30 seconds, gently removed, wiped clean quickly and the reading taken. Average temperature for horses is 38°C.

Bodyweight

Too fat and too thin are both bad! You shouldn't be able to see the ribs, but should be able to feel them quite easily. The spine should be well covered with flesh, without being fat.

The skin-pinch test

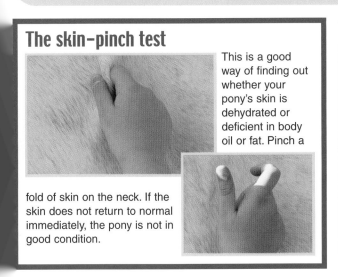

This is a good way of finding out whether your pony's skin is dehydrated or deficient in body oil or fat. Pinch a fold of skin on the neck. If the skin does not return to normal immediately, the pony is not in good condition.

Take it to another level

Check out this condition scoring diagram to make sure your pony is neither too fat nor too thin. The diagram shows the extremes of being too thin (hips protruding, prominent croup) or too fat.

Hollow area along spine

Prominent croup

Too fat

Large pads of fat

Too thin

Protruding hips

Heather longed to be a good rider, just like her mum, but her nerves held her back

scared to ride!

Posed by models

I've always loved horses and ponies. My dream was always to be a really good rider, but there was one problem: I was scared of my pony.

My mum and Dad ride, too. My mum used to event her horse when she was younger and so, of course, she was keen for me to follow in her footsteps. It wasn't too bad when I was very young, mainly because I rode at the riding school. The instructress was great and she never pushed me. My troubles started when Mum and Dad bought me a pony of my own. A young pony, only four years old.

His name was Marlon, he was 14hh, chestnut and part Welsh. He looked lovely but he was very, very green. We kept him at home – Mum's old eventer Tyrone kept him company in the field – and Mum looked after him. I had to ride him, though.

At first it wasn't too bad. Marlon was quite well behaved in our paddock at home and Mum would teach me. But after a couple of weeks, Mum expected me to ride Marlon on my own. She had other things to do. So I started well enough, but I soon ran out of things to do, and Marlon grew bored and restless. Instead of behaving himself, Marlon started to nap towards the paddock gate, or snatch grass when I wasn't paying attention – almost pulling me out of the saddle. When Mum was with me, he was always well behaved, he seemed to know I was a bit of a soft touch, and he took advantage of me when we were alone. When Mum came out, she would shout at me and I'd ride him a bit better, but when she wasn't there, things just got worse and worse.

I started to dread riding Marlon and doing anything with him. I couldn't tell Mum how I felt, she was determined I should ride and be really good at it. I got more and more miserable.

One day, when Mum was teaching me, she told me to use my stick because Marlon was going too slow. So I did, and Marlon took off with me across the paddock, stopping dead at the gate. I slid off. I didn't hurt myself, but Mum had a right go at me, telling me to get back on

and show Marlon who was boss. Well, I knew who was boss – and it wasn't me! I did re-mount, but Marlon was so naughty with me, I couldn't ride him for much longer and Mum had to get on him and get him going well. He behaved perfectly for her.

"I don't understand what you find so difficult, Heather," Mum said. "He's not bad, just a bit naughty. He's only young and it's up to you to teach him to be good." I wanted riding to be fun and riding Marlon was anything but that!

> ## I started to dread riding Marlon... but I couldn't tell Mum how I felt

The next day, I had a bit of a stomach bug, so Mum said I didn't have to ride. The day after, I felt fine but when Mum asked me, I said I still felt ill. It was great, I didn't have to ride Marlon. I was happy – and he definitely was. He hated me. Well, I couldn't have a stomach bug forever, but after that I said I'd hurt my finger at school, said I'd shut it in a door.

I managed a whole week without riding, and then I knew I'd have to face it again. But then I had another idea: I'd ride past the house, but Mum couldn't see me when I was in the paddock. I just got off and let Marlon graze. It was another week before Mum found out. I thought she'd be angry but instead, she wanted to know the reason why I'd deceived her. She seemed really upset. I blurted it all out – how I felt scared and useless on Marlon, and how I could never be a good rider like her. I told her I'd let her down.

I expected Mum to be disappointed in me. In fact, when I told her how I felt, I realised I was upset more because I wasn't such a good rider as she was. It wasn't only that I was scared of riding Marlon, I didn't want to let Mum down. Her reaction surprised me, though. She told me she never realised how I'd felt and that she'd always been pushed hard as a child. I was astonished.

We hugged and Mum told me I didn't

> ## I wanted riding to be fun and riding Marlon was anything but that!

have to ride Marlon again if I hated it so much. When she said it, I felt like a huge weight had been lifted from my shoulders. But then, something strange happened: I decided I *wanted* to learn to ride Marlon. Now I didn't *have* to, I didn't want to run away from my fears. I explained this to Mum and she looked really proud. I realised I had always wanted to make her proud of me – and in this way, I had.

"We'll get you a more suitable pony to ride," she told me.

"But I want to learn to ride Marlon. I don't want him to beat me!" I said.

"You will, but you need something else to get confident on. Honestly, Heather, you will ride Marlon. I promise!"

That was a year ago. We got a lovely mare called Callie who gave me lots of confidence, and between riding her, I tackled Marlon. Me and Mum go riding together now – we can both ride either pony, so we swap over.

I love riding now. Callie's lovely – and I've even grown to love Marlon. He's a cheeky monkey, just a youngster who needs firm handling, and I'm learning to be stronger with him. The best bit is, me and Mum are really good friends. Marlon tore us apart for a while, but he's brought us back together again!

There are readers' real-life experiences every month in PONY Magazine!

31

ON THE RIGHT TACK!

So you think you know about saddles and bridles? Check out your tack knowledge below – turn to page 98 to find out how you scored.

1 Can you name these parts of the saddle? We've scrambled up the letters to give you a clue!

lmpmoe - swtia - cltnae - plfa - teas

_____

_____

_____

_____

_____

2 Do you know the names of these parts of the bridle? Unscramble the letters to find out!

hlstorhata - ndrbowab - sbeonnda - hepeecikec - ciepehdea - nrie

_____

_____

_____

_____

_____

_____

3 Check these photos and write down what's wrong with the way the tack has been fitted.

A_____

_____

C_____

_____

B_____

_____

_____

_____

D_____

_____

E_____

_____

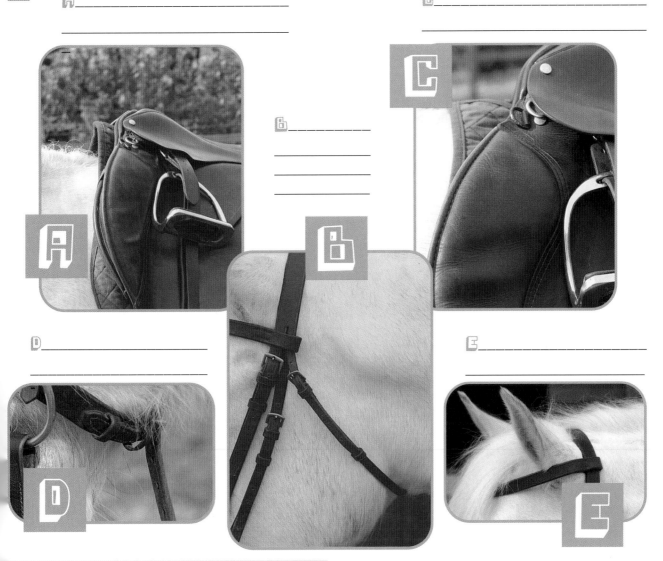

4 Can you answer these tack fitting questions?

a) Describe how you can tell whether the throatlash is fastened at the right length?

_____

b) How do you know if the bit is fitted too high or too low?

_____

c) When a saddle is on a horse's back, it should not touch the spine at all – you should be able to see a clear channel of daylight down the spine from withers to loins. True or false?

_____

d) When you do up the girth, which of the three girth straps on the saddle should you attach it to?

_____

e) Why is it important to ensure that a drop noseband is not fitted too low?

_____

5 Answer 'true' or 'false' to these questions:

a) Double bridles have three bits
❏ True ❏ False

b) A hackamore is a type of bitless bridle
❏ True ❏ False

c) Dressage saddles are forward cut to make jumping easier
❏ True ❏ False

d) Throatlashes are needed to keep the bridle on a pony's head
❏ True ❏ False

e) A Flash is a type of martingale
❏ True ❏ False

Now turn to page 98 to discover how well you have done!

10

WAYS TO BE YOUR PONY'S BEST FRIEND

Want to be best friends with your fave pony? Want him to listen for the sound of your voice? Follow our fab advice and he'll soon love you just as much as you love him!

1. Speak softly

Ponies have good hearing and there's no need to shout. Instead, talk softly to your fave pony – you can have a private conversion and no one will know. Best friends don't shout!

2. Move with confidence

Ponies can get irritated by people who hesitate and creep about. Make your movements deliberate, without being jerky or sudden. Breathe evenly and your confidence will soar – and so will your fave pony's confidence in you.

3. Be firm!

Ponies can be a bit cheeky, and they respect people who are firm with them. You don't have to be harsh, or tell them off, just make it clear what you want, and expect to get it. That way, any pony will enjoy being with you. Just as all your best friends do!

4. Give treats!

Everyone knows that ponies love food! Make sure you give treats only when they have been earned, or in the special moments you share together. That way, your pony will know you appreciate him, and not expect you to feed him all the time. And make sure the treats are pony-friendly!

5. Ride as well as you can!

Ponies appreciate clarity - so when you ride, make your aids clear. Also, see how little you need to do (do you really need to kick so hard?) to get what you want. Ride each pony as an individual to get the very best out of them. All the ponies will ask for you again!

6. What does he like?

Take time to discover what your fave pony enjoys. Does he like you scratching him in a certain way, or having his eyes rubbed? Or he might enjoy you singing to him, or telling him a story. Watch his eyes and ears to discover what he like! Friends always take time to do things for one another.

7. Be considerate

Are you polite? You often see people being very rude to their horses and ponies, never asking them anything, just pushing them around and shouting at them. Ponies can't enjoy their company at all! Think about how you like to be treated, and do the same for your fave pony. He'll definitely like that!

8. Be loyal

Friends are always loyal to one another, so make sure the same applies to you and your fave pony. Stick up for him if others say rude things about him. If he's naughty, see whether he is hurting anywhere, or he may be a bit off-colour. He'll never be your best friend if you don't stand by him.

9. Have boundaries

He's your friend, but that doesn't mean he can barge all over you. So make sure your pony respects your space; don't let him nudge you, rub on you or step on your toes. He'll have no respect for you if you don't respect yourself.

10. Say thanks

Everyone likes to be appreciated - and ponies are no exception. Giving your pony a pat when he'd done well is a lovely thing to do - and it will make you both feel good - and his confidence will grow as fast as his love for you!

Blond bombshells
– with beauty, brains and brawn!

Origins

The original home of the Haflinger is the town of Hafling, in southern Austria. They are considered to be cold-blooded horses (laid-back, hardy types), although four of the breed's five principal bloodlines can be traced back to the Arab stallion, El Bedavi, who was imported from Arabia in the 19th Century. The mountain conditions in which they originate have ensured that Haflingers are hardy, sure-footed, and more than capable of working as pack horses on steep mountain slopes.

Quality control

In Austria, all Haflinger stallions are kept at state-owned studs. At three years old, all Haflingers are inspected and graded before they are chosen for breeding, so that only the very best characteristics are passed on to future generations, and the breed remains as wonderful as it is today. The Edelweiss brand mark (an H inside the shape of an Edelweiss flower) is used to show fully registered and inspected breeding Haflingers.

Haflingers in the UK

The Duchess of Devonshire founded the Haflinger Society of Great Britain in 1970. The society organises inspections, just like those in Austria, so that Haflingers bred in Great Britain maintain the qualities of the original breed. There are also breed shows and Haflinger studs in the UK – check out www.haflingergb.com to discover more!

Did you know?
In Austria, the Haflinger doesn't start working until it is four years old. However, they can go on forever, and it's not uncommon for them to work into their 40s!

Did you know?
The Queen was given two Haflingers during a state visit to Austria!

The Haflinger is an amazing all-round pony with looks to die for! From the mountains of Austria, Haflingers are the ultimate equine 4x4!

Fact file

Height: 13.1-15hh
Colour: Always chestnut, with a flaxen mane and tail.
Temperament: Friendly, quiet, people-loving.
Characteristics: Strong with powerful quarters. Well muscled, but elegant, too.
Ideal for: Anything – the Haflinger is a real all-rounder!

Why we love 'em

PONY model Folly is a Haflinger. She's fun, reliable and really glam! We love Folly because she has great paces, works well on the flat and is fab at jumping, too! She's sensible enough for beginners to ride, but fast and challenging for more competent riders. Plus, being a Haflinger means she's strong enough to carry an adult!

Folly's done just about everything. She's been to Pony Club camp, done BSJA jumping, competed in one-day events and dressage. Folly even goes on holiday to the Isle of Wight! And, better than all of that, she's great fun to be around.

Did you know?
The Haflinger is sometimes called the Edelweiss pony, because of the flower emblem (right) they are branded with.

Destiny

By PONY reader Devon Edwards Joseph

Carla Louise was born into a showjumping family – but this wasn't just any old family. Oh no. Carla was a member of the *Charsington* family. They were the world-famous, most well-known showjumping family to ever compete. So good were the Charsingtons, it was said that other competitors actually packed-up and left the showground in despair whenever they saw them arrive at the show!

In every family there is an odd-ball. Carla was the Charsington odd-ball. She had no interest in horses (even though she could ride), and the term 'cob' still meant a bread roll to her! Her inheritance of horsy knowledge was as scarcely seen as the word *lose* was heard in and around the Charsington stables.

The showjumping season had just begun, and the atmosphere at the showground at the first show of the season was tense. Everyone's heads turned to face the priceless horse lorry which pulled into the horsebox park. It took its place next to the other lorries, but it looked out of place, being more used to the surroundings of more well-known showgrounds. Carla slumped out of the side door of the lorry and looked for a tree to hide under. She found one next to the practice ring, and began listening to her Ipod. Half asleep, she was shaken awake by a hysterical looking woman – Carla's mother.

"We've found you the perfect horse on which you can start your competing career!" she cried. "It came second to your father in the jump-off, and I just *had* to have him. Come and see him, Carla!" Her mother dragged Carla over to a small shaded area and under the canopy stood an overweight Connemara.

"Mum, how on earth did that thing ever come second to Father?" Carla asked, astounded.

"No silly, that's his travel mate, they're inseparable. Look over there..."

Carla looked. There stood a glossy black stallion, with a flowing tail and the most stunning conformation ever seen!

"He's yours, Carla!" her mother shrieked. Carla stared at the horse. It tossed its mane and stared at her with piercing eyes.

Under the canopy stood an overweight Connemara...

"I prefer the other one," said Carla, turning away from the stallion, and showing no sign of being impressed.

"Oh come on, darling," cried her mother..."

"No, I prefer the other one!" yelled Carla, annoyed.

"Okay, darling," Carla's mother said, "but only if you promise you will jump the stallion in competitions."

"Whatever..." sighed Carla, and she walked off to find a fast-food stand.

The next morning, Carla came onto the yard feeling even more depressed than usual, now she had agreed to start competing. But there was no large glossy stallion waiting for her, only the tubby little Connemara – the stallion's friend. She had almost forgotten that she now had to look after him. A groom held the rope attached to the pony's fancy leather headcollar, which looked totally out of place on the pony's little face. Grabbing the rope from the man, Carla pulled the pony round to the paddocks at the back of the yard. She tied the pony to the fence, and walked off to get a saddle and bridle. Although she didn't want to ride the pony, she found pleasure in the thought of seeing the expression on her parents' faces if the daughter of two top show jumpers were spotted on a fat plodder. She roughly knew how to put on tack, although she had to call a groom to help her with the bridle.

Carla kicked the pony and, to her surprise, it set off at a brisk trot

Climbing into the polished saddle, she kicked the pony and, to her surprise, it set off at a brisk trot.

"Whoa," you may be fat, but you're not lazy, are you fatty?"

Carla thought for a moment. "Hey, maybe I should call you Fatty. After all, it suits you fine!"

At that moment, Carla's mother appeared from around the corner and the stable yard was filled with her ear-piercing scream.

The next show day loomed, and this was to be Carla's showjumping debut. She was entered to ride in the four o'clock class. Carla had persuaded her mother to let her bring 'her Fatty' along, by refusing to ride otherwise.

Her mother hauled herself up onto her favourite horse, a 16.2hh chestnut mare

with a notorious temper, and set off to the practice ring at a perfect canter. Carla watched after her, and started to feel anxious about her first ride on the black stallion. She walked round to the lorry, where the stallion was being prepared for her. Next to him was Fatty, pawing the ground for treats.

"You're not having any, stupid," sneered Carla, "you're already 10 times your recommended weight at least!" This made her feel better.

Suddenly, Carla heard the noise of horses' hooves coming from the collecting ring. The horse was coming straight for her – it was her mother's chestnut mare! Carla froze. The horse was galloping full speed towards her, and Carla could hear the screams of spectators and the other riders. Skidding to a halt in front of Carla, it rose high into the air, its hooves flashing in front of her, inches from her face.

But then, something amazing happened; Fatty jumped forward as long as his rope would allow, and aimed his hind hooves at the mare. Caught off-guard, she fell onto the ground, her hooves churning up the ground. Before Carla could do anything, the horse got back up and bucked wildly, targeting anything within reach. Carla cried out, "The black stallion, she's going to kick him!" but it happened too fast for anyone to stop it. The mare caught the stallion across his front leg with a sickening thud.

When the vet had treated the black stallion, he talked to Carla's mother. "I'm afraid he won't be able to compete toda he'll need rest for at least a week, maybe more," he sighed.

"But he was due to jump today!" exclaimed Carla's mother.

Moving away from the commotion, Carla was still shocked by what had happened. The little fat Connemara had saved her, protected her from the crazy chestnut mare. Carla's mother came rushing over;

"Carla, you are going to have to ride a different horse, the black one isn't going to be able to help your debut in the ring."

"I'll ride Fatty," said Carla.

"Don't be silly, that fat, ugly little thing will never get over a jump. How embarrassing would that be? Think of the damage to our reputation!" It was no use; Carla's mind was made up and she stood firm. She remembered the way the pony had been so responsive when she had first ridden him.

As the class started, Carla sat aboard Fatty, having serious second thoughts about what she was doing. She couldn't ignore the dirty and confused looks she was getting from the other competitors, and she could hear them sniggering.

The jumps were not high, but the course was long and complicated, with lots of twists and turns and a small water jump.

It was her turn to jump. Entering the ring at a fast canter, she slowed the pony slightly, and headed him towards the first jump. She suddenly realised the enormity of what she was doing; she had a fat pony and she didn't know whether he could jump, and she was in front of lots of expectant Charsington fans (not to mention enemies)! But it was too late now, she had to ride on and have a go at the course, whatever the cost.

The pony picked up speed towards the first jump and leapt into the air too early. This unnerved Carla, and she gulped, pushing the pony on to the next jump. He skidded up to it, and cat-leapt it at the last moment.

"This is terrible," thought Carla, "and everybody is watching me!" But she was amazed at Fatty's jumping ability. He could really leap!

They were now approaching the most complicated jump on the course, an upright of shark's teeth. She had never

"Carla, you are going to have to ride a different horse..."

jumped anything like this in training, and she could feel the pony hesitating under her. Urging him on, she counted herself into the jump, three, two, one and over! The perfect jump! The rest of the course was over as fast as it started and Carla had to do barely any riding as the pony cleared the jumps with ease. She brought him back to a walk outside the ring and slid off, narrowly avoiding being knocked over by her hysterical mother.

"That was brilliant, you cleared the shark's teeth effortlessly, and the water – just like a professional!"

Everyone gathered around to hear the placings. *Third place, Laura Ebbsworth and Gilmore's Gift... second place, Sarah Greensby and Miss Tiny Toe, and first place goes to ... Carla Charsington and... Fatty!* A roar of laughter and applause followed. Fatty received more pats and cuddles than he could ever had hoped for (not to mention treats), and Carla almost had the life squeezed out of her by all the hugs and congratulations. She had fulfilled her destiny. It wasn't quite as her mother had imagined, still...

So you see, there is no longer one odd-ball at the Charsington Stables. Now there are two!

Posed by models

THREE, TWO, ONE AND OVER! THE PERFECT JUMP!

What is vaulting?

Vaulting is gymnastics on horseback! The horse canters in a circle, controlled by a person in the centre, who holds the lunge line. The vaulters jump on and off the horse as it canters around! **The great thing about vaulting is that lots of people can join in – but you only need one horse!**

Why vault?

It's great fun! Vaulting teaches balance, confidence and harmony with the horse – as well as strength, poise, grace and co-ordination. How cool would it be to be able to run and jump onto the back of a cantering horse – not forgetting jumping off again! It is also a great team sport – vaulters work with one another in teams in competitions.

Count the vaulters!

Vaulters start off slowly!

Did you know?

Stone paintings dating from Scandinavia in 1500BC show people standing up on horses – could these have been the very first people to vault?

It's an ancient art!

Vaulting was seen in the games in Ancient Rome over 2000 years ago. Acrobatic and dance movements on cantering horses were seen by Julius Caesar!

Go for gold!

Known at the time as Artistic Riding, Vaulting was included in the Olympic Games in 1920. Belgium took the team gold medal, with France (silver) and Sweden (bronze).

Facing backwards isn't a mistake in vaulting!

Vaulting as we know it now...

Modern vaulting was popular in Germany after the second World War. It wasn't until the 60s that vaulting became popular in the rest of Europe and the USA.

Vaulting goes showbiz!

Rebecca Townsend started vaulting when she was just 12 years old. She went on to become British Champion – a title she held for six years! Rebecca has taken her vaulting to another level, she and her wonderful Highland pony, Ronan, are Jive Pony – a fabulous vaulting/circus display!

Rebecca has trained Ronan to perform without the aid of a lunger, and here are just a few of the moves they get up to!

Rebecca and Ronan obviously enjoy a close bond.

you think vaulting is for you then log on to www.vaulting.org.uk!

find out more about Jive Pony, log on to www.jive-pony.co.uk.

Remember!
Always try a new sport under supervision. Never try vaulting without the help of a proper Vaulting Group or instructor and specially trained horse. PONY Magazine recommends everyone wears a properly fitted, approved riding hat when riding.

Charlie-up your sa

How to do it!

Cut out our paper patterns of Charlie (x two), his shades and nostrils. Or trace them onto paper if you'd rather not cut your annual!

3

You'll be left with these shapes, ready to assemble as Charlie!

1

4

2

Pin these to the felt – Charlie to the fawn felt, shades and nostrils to the black felt. Pin the extra pattern of Charlie to the wadding. Cut them all out.

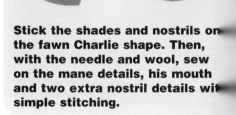

Stick the shades and nostrils on the fawn Charlie shape. Then, with the needle and wool, sew on the mane details, his mouth and two extra nostril details wit simple stitching.

42

...dlecloth!

Make a fabulous Charlie motif for your fave pony's saddlecloth!

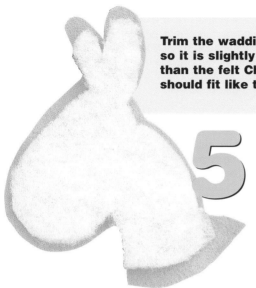

Trim the wadding Charlie so it is slightly smaller than the felt Charlie. It should fit like this!

5

6

Pin Charlie, with his wadding underneath, on your saddle cloth. Then, start sewing him on.

7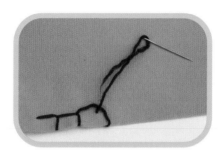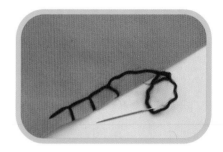

▲ **Use blanket stitch – this is how you do it!**

8

When you've finished, Charlie will be sewn to your saddle cloth!

9

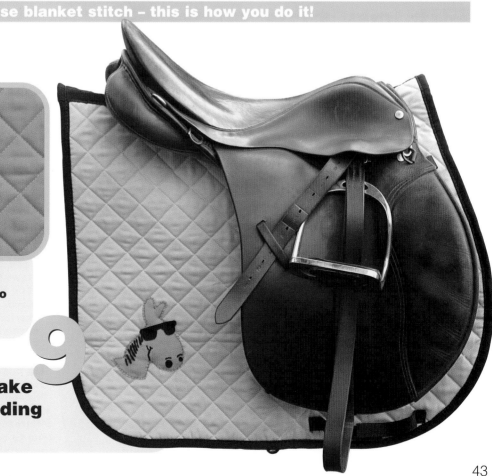

Now, you can take Charlie along riding with you!

If you think western riding is just about putting on a pair of jeans and a cowboy hat, you can think again! Western riding is *sooo* different from English. For a start, the reins aren't nearly as important because the rider tells his horse everything he needs to know with his weight. Complicated turns and spins can be performed by a small shift in the rider's weight and through neck reining, which is where the rider moves the rein from one side of the neck to the other. Good western horses can perform movements like a sliding stop from a flat-out gallop, without the rider having to use the action of the bit – how cool is that?

Traditionally, Quarter horses are used for western. They are famous for being the fastest breed of horse to gallop a quarter-of-a mile from a standing start, and they also possess a natural ability to work with cattle, making them the equine equivalent of a sheep dog!

There are lots of different western competitions which are all based on the traditional techniques used by cowboys to look after cattle. Reining classes are a bit like dressage tests, but with turns and spins. They test how obedient and accurate the horse and rider are.

Cutting is when a rider must separate a specific steer (cow) from the herd of cattle, this originates from the need to brand individual steers. There are also trail competitions, which test the horse's suitability to ride through any terrain and natural obstacles they might encounter on a trail ride, and takes the form of an obstacle course type of competition.

Way out west!

Go do it!

Bit on the side

If you love period dramas, you'll love riding side-saddle! It's ultra glamorous, and really good fun. The side saddle evolved in the 16th century. Before this, women sat sideways on little more than a pad, and so had to be led about everywhere by men!

Women always wore dresses, and therefore it was far too un-lady like for them to consider riding astride. When the side saddle we know today, with its stirrup, cantle and pommel was developed it didn't just give women security in the saddle, it gave women the independence they wanted.

Side saddles are so secure that by the time the 19th century arrived, women were often seen riding beside men on the hunting field. It wasn't until the change in the role of women at the time of the Second World War that made them equal to men that women started riding astride in the type of saddles we use today.

When you sit on a side saddle it's important that your weight is central, otherwise you'll make your pony uncomfortable. The right thigh goes across the saddle and hooks over the upper pommel and the left leg sits under the lower pommel (or leaping head). The rider uses a whip in the right hand, instead of the leg aid, and the left leg is used as you would normally ride.

When you're jumping or if you need some extra security, the left leg pushes up towards the lower pommel to hold the rider in place. The rein contact is the same as in traditional riding, and the only other difference is that side saddle riders tend to sit to the trot as it's more comfortable than rising!

Make music!

Riding to music is a great way of bonding with your fave pony and gives you the chance to ride with your mates, too! There are lots of different ways you can do it, from a musical ride with loads of horses, like the fabulous mounted police display team which you may have seen at Olympia, to going solo like Anky van Grunsven in the Kür with her famous routines on the enchanting horse, Bonfire. Don't worry, you don't have to be super-high powered to give it a go – if you can ride a simple dressage test or routine you have made up, and have access to a tape player, you've got all the ingredients necessary to give it a go!

The first thing you need to do is make up a routine. Include all the things you can do well, like circles, changes of rein and riding down the centre line. Try not to include too many changes of pace, as this makes recording your music more complicated. Next, you need to find some music which goes with your pony's paces – try riding with your MP3 player, or if you can get someone to video you riding you can do this at home! Instrumental music is best, so you don't have to worry about mixing the words.

When you've decided on your music and your routine, you need to time how long each piece of music needs to be – you can do this with a stop watch, or using a video of you riding. Next, record each piece of music back-to-back, for the right amount of time. Now you can ride your routine to the tape you've made and enjoy making your pony dance!

Have you ever thought about doing something a bit different? There's so much more to riding than plodding round the sand school that PONY thought it was time we gave you the low-down on some of the most exciting ways to be around horses, so that you can go and do it!

Driving ambition

Scurry driving is fast, furious and great fun! It's like racing round an obstacle course, only you have ponies to do the hard work, a vehicle to sit on, and a groom hanging off the back to help you keep your balance! The aim is to drive through the course as quickly as you can, without knocking any of the cones. For each cone you hit, time is added on so sometimes it pays to be slow but careful.

Usually, scurry ponies are small and race in pairs, but you find all sorts of scurry teams! You can see them at the Horse of the Year Show and other big shows, but if you want to get into it, it's best to start with the basics and learn how to drive ponies.

When ponies are driven, they wear a special sort of tack called a harness. The bridles they use are fairly similar but they have blinkers, to stop the pony from spooking at anything behind him, and a driving bit. The reins go through special loops called terrets on the saddle, which is like a roller. The ponies wear collars round their necks and the traces fastens to the collars and the vehicle so that the ponies can pull it along. The brakes are supplied by the breeching, which fits round the pony's quarters and stops the vehicle from rolling into them when they're going down hill.

When you drive a pony, you hold both reins in the left hand and the driving whip in your right hand. This allows you to quickly shorten the reins in an emergency. The groom on the back helps to keep the vehicle in balance, and they hold the ponies when they stop, so that the driver can get out of the vehicle without having to let go of the ponies.

shhhhh!
pony whispering

You know how it is… you can't get your pony to do anything you ask it to do. You're starting to get angry through frustration. Then along comes someone else who seems to do nothing more than say a few quiet words, make a few small actions – and, hey presto! – your pony is obediently following her commands.

> So what is it that enables some people to handle ponies effectively and others not?
> **Follow our six-step plan to find out!**

Stay calm!

There's one golden rule that should be top of your list all the time – if you are calm you will achieve much, much more than if you lose your cool. Some of us find it easier than others to stay calm. If you tend to get cross quickly, try breathing in and out slowly and deeply, or counting to 10 before doing anything. Breathing slowly in this way will calm both of you as horses 'pick up' on this.

Angry!

Very calm!

1

Your voice **2**

Horses respond quickly to the voice. A calm, soothing word will calm an excitable or worried horse. If you shout angrily, that will have an unnerving effect. Humming can have a relaxing effect on horses, so try this out. When you approach or touch a pony, speak quietly to him so that he knows you are there – this will prevent him from being startled.

Be consistent **3**

You need to set ground rules for the way you expect your pony to behave, and then stick by them. It's no good expecting a pony to stand still when you mount him one day, but let him get away with wandering off the next. They need to understand clearly what you want, and consistency is the way to achieve this. If you are not consistent, and get cross about something one time but not another, you will end up with a very confused pony. Eventually, unless he's a saint, he'll get stroppy and you'll have a problem on your hands.

Move that body!

Ponies are very sensitive to our body language, and you can use this knowledge to get ponies to react in certain ways.

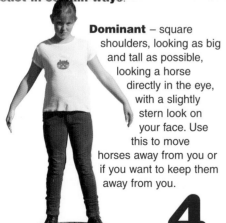

Dominant – square shoulders, looking as big and tall as possible, looking a horse directly in the eye, with a slightly stern look on your face. Use this to move horses away from you or if you want to keep them away from you.

4

Positive – this is a confident, but softer and less stern look; eyes looking straight ahead, but gently smiling. A good posture for most of your horse handling because it makes horses feel confident in you and therefore secure with you around.

Passive – your body turned away slightly, your gaze lowered. This encourages the pony to come towards you as it will not feel threatened or dominated by you.

Paint a positive picture

5

If you're positive and cheerful in the way you handle your pony, he is likely to be too! Horses and ponies are sensitive to our moods and feelings, and will pick up our negative and positive vibes. Even if you are worried about doing something with him – maybe he isn't easy to catch in his field – try to picture a positive outcome, as this will make you *feel* more positive. If you are positive, he is likely to be, too! It's worth actually visualising the thing you are trying to do. For example, if you know that your pony won't want to be caught in his field, try to picture in your mind a positive picture of him with his headcollar on, being led happily back to his stable. You will be amazed at the difference it can make!

Praise and encourage

6

Always praise good behaviour – this is *positive reinforcement*. Most horses want to do their best for you, and love to be told they have done the right thing. A warm pat on the neck, accompanied by the words 'Good boy/girl' said in a positive, happy way, goes down a treat.

If you have problems either handling or riding your pony, get help from an expert or your instructor. They will be able to tell you why your pony is not obeying you and what to do about it. And make it a golden rule that you never – ever – hit a pony in anger or lose your temper with him.

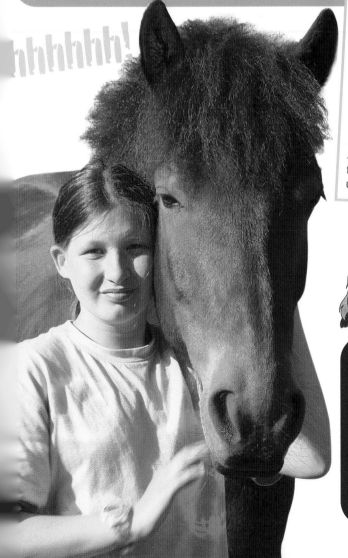

Pony handling

Being aware of all these techniques will help you when you are handling ponies. It's important, too, that you learn as much as you can about how to handle them so that you go about this in a safe, calm and positive way. If you fumble when you are doing up a headcollar, or trying to get a bridle on, ponies soon get to know that you don't know what you are doing – and will start to play up.

Read as much as you can in PONY **magazine** and in books, ask for advice from experienced people, and practise doing things properly. There's always something to learn, however experienced you are – which is what makes pony handling so fascinating.

Pony Professor

Check what you've learnt!
What can you do to stop a horse coming closer to you?

Try using your hand, palm facing the horse, held up in front of you, between you and the horse. This gives a clear signal to help stop him from coming closer.

Duggie's do's & don'ts

Do make sure you understand ponies' language – see p. 8 for more on this.
Don't make any sudden movements – it's guaranteed to make a horse jump a mile.
Do feed titbits from time to time as a reward, but not so often that the pony expects one. If he does, he'll start to nibble your clothing, or even you – and then get confused when you tell him off for doing this!

... they go really fast! Nothing like a blast on the grass to clear the cobwebs and get the adrenaline going! The freedom a pony gives you when you go for a ride with your friends is unbeatable!

... you can smarten them up when you're feeling creative. They're not dolls, but it's great fun to give them a trim, a wash and brush up, and then plait their manes and tails. It's a fabulous way to spend time together!

... they never say "because I said so," or "told you so...!" Ponies are wise without rubbing your nose in it – and you hope some of that wisdom rubs off onto you!

... they open up a whole new world of responsibility. Ponies are fun, but they also teach you to put their needs before your own. Keeping a pony teaches you lots of life skills, and these can equip you for the rest of your life!

... they're your best friends. Just sharing a hack or a lesson gives you the feeling of belonging to an exclusive team of two. It's you and your pony against the rest of the world, and you'll never let each other down.

... because they never bear a grudge. You fave pony never sulks, or reminds you ho you were rough with him when you were in a bad mood, or pulled him in the mouth by mistake when you went jumping. Ponies are forgiving – they're big-hearte and you wish you were like them.

... they're always there for you when you're feeling down. You might have had a bad day at school or had a row with your best friend, but your fave pony will always be there to listen to your woes and help you through the difficult times.

... they're simply the best. No argument! Done deal.

Charlie goes visiting

Ooh – a letter for me!

"Dear Charlie, we would love you to come and visit us..."

Oh Charlie, my sister Ethel is lovely. You must go to stay!

Charlie, you *can't* need all those clothes!

Woo hoo! I'm going on holiday!

I'm so bored now, how much longer is this flight going to take?

You must be cousin Bruce!

G'day Charlie!

G'day Charlie, welcome to Australia! I'm your aunt Ethel. This is your uncle Stanley and your cousin Sheila.

Australia is great. The weather is fab and the fillies love me!

Charlie, come and play volleyball with us!

Mum, it's so cool here.

Well say hello to Ethel for me. I'm glad you're having so much fun, dear!

We're having a 'barbie' tomorrow. Gotta go, Mum!

So what are we doing tomorrow, Bruce?

Well, mate, I thought we'd go to Uluru. It's the huge rock...

Yeah, I've read about it. I can't wait!

Wow! It's enormous!

Come on, we'd better start walking or it'll be dark before we get to the top!

Charlie, be careful. There are loads of kangaroos around here.

It's OK, I just want to get a good pic of the view. I'll be back in a sec!

Uh-oh! Bruce? Sheila?

Aargh!

What happened?

You wandered off the path and into a kangaroo.

Kangaroos are dangerous, Charlie. You could have been badly hurt.

Back home

Charlene! That is so mean!

Oh come on Charlie, it's only a toy!

Humph!

50

Karen thought her pony Smudge was just perfect – but one day, he turned into a wild thing!

the day my pony went mad!

Smudge is my pony – and he's just ace! Smudge is always the perfect gentleman, and we've always been a bit of a team. We've enjoyed cross country together, done the odd bit of showjumping, and even tried dressage. He'll have a go at anything, and that's one of the reasons why I love him so much.

Smudge and I usually ride out with our friends Julie and her pony Pippin. Pippin can be a bit naughty at times, and although Smudge dances about when Pippin starts his napping and shying routine, he's usually a good influence. The thing about Smudge is, whereas Pippin will sometimes put in a nasty buck and unseat Julie, Smudge would never do anything like that. Like I said, he's a gentleman. But then one day, something happened to drive Smudge to be Mr Hyde, instead of his usual nice Dr Jekyll!

I was supposed to be going riding with Julie, as usual. But

> One moment, we were dawdling along enjoying the sunshine and the next, Smudge turned into a demon

then she called me on my mobile to say she'd had a toothache all night and was going to the dentist. Well, it was such a lovely day that I decided to go for a ride anyway, just me and Smudge. The weather was warm so I decided not to do too much or go too far.

We set off along the bridleways and we had a short canter in a meadow, but then Smudge broke out into a sweat so I walked him into the cool of the woods. The sun filtered through the trees and made dapples on the ground, it was like an enchanted wood, and I told Smudge to look out for fairies!

We were just about to head for home when it happened; one moment, we were dawdling along enjoying the sunshine and the next, Smudge turned into a demon. His head went up, his tail clamped down and he took off through the trees like a rodeo horse, bucking and broncing. I was caught completely by surprise, but managed to gather up my reins, which had been in loops, and shouted "Whoa Smudge, steady there...". I lost a stirrup and thought I was going to fall off, but gripped with my knees as tightly as I could. I knew it was only a matter of time before I fell off. Lots of images flashed through my mind; Smudge running blindly on the road, or slipping on the tarmac, or ... the images went on and on, and suddenly I lost my grip and flew through the air, landing on the ground with a thump.

I sat up to see Smudge disappear in the direction of home. He was still bucking

> I lost a stirrup and thought I was going to fall off, but gripped with my knees as tightly as I could.

and snorting and I could see his reins dangling around his legs. Whatever could have made him react so violently? I couldn't imagine, but then I realised that my arm hurt like mad!

I managed to get myself to my feet and nursed my throbbing arm. My head hurt, too, but my hat had saved me from injury. Thank goodness! I ran after Smudge. My knee was hurting as well, but I was so scared for my pony. What could have made him do what he did? It was so out of character. Something was wrong with him – I just hoped it wasn't serious. I rang the yard from my mobile, and everyone there said they would set out looking for my pony and me, and it wasn't long before someone came with a Land Rover to pick me up.

"Smudge is at the yard – he's all in one piece," said Tom, the yard owner.

"He just went mad – bucking and squealing, I don't know what was the matter with him," I said.

"I think we know – he has a huge lump on his thigh, we think he's been stung by something," Tom told me.

I was really relieved; I thought my perfect pony had gone mad. Poor Smudge, he had obviously been in a lot of pain and couldn't help himself.

When I got back to the yard, Smudge was still trembling. The vet came out and agreed that he'd been stung, but thought he would be alright. I got taken to the hospital and had to sit in casualty for ages, just to make sure my arm wasn't broken. It wasn't!

Poor Smudge. The sting must have really hurt him, and I felt so sorry for him. He looked really sheepish the next day, and nuzzled me when I went to see him. He couldn't help being so naughty, and I forgave him.

> He just went mad – bucking and squealing, I don't know what was the matter with him

We're still the best of friends, but I use a lot more insect repellent when I go riding now! I hope our adventure was a one-off experience. Smudge is still my perfect pony – and I appreciate him even more now I know how high he can buck!

Posed by models

There are readers' real-life experiences every month in PONY Magazine!

Quirky Quiz!

Find the words!

Can you find the following words in our wordsearch? They have been cunningly hidden going vertically, horizontally, diagonally – and backwards or forwards in any direction.

Words to find:

Wither	Pony
Throatlash	Trot
Vet	Bridle
Hat	Reins
Snaffle	Hoofpick

```
w n s u d p j r i l r f y
m y n o p b a o v r o g t
y j a w l e m e a n s t h
j e f b a a t h a t r i r
n q f f w n s u v t l m o
i b l p s s f m u l c s a
s i e t n t i u k e y t t
r g o i k r s e r x s r l
b t e c a e h r a s c e a
b r i d l e o l n z y b s
f o l e h o o f p i c k h
a t d d l y o a i i g r i
l t w i t h e r e h c r p
```

Mystery word

Work out the answers to the clues to reveal the mystery word in the vertical panel.

1. The back of a saddle
2. This pony comes from Norway
3. A very serious veterinary condition that affects the hooves (often caused by eating too much spring grass)
4. Also called an ass
5. Beautiful orangey-gold horse colour
6. Long hair on horses' necks

7. Ponies wear this when they are being ridden
8. A giant of a horse!
9. Poisonous plant with yellow flowers

Spot the difference

There are six differences between these two photos. Can you spot them?

Match boxes

Match up the boxes in pairs to find 10 different horsy words. We've done the first pair to get you going!

can	ter	ses
ene	dig	key
sta	jac	ies
rgy	ble	hor
ter	win	est
don	pon	ket

| c | a | n | t | e | r | | | | | |

General Knowledge

Test your horse knowledge and see if you can answer the questions below. Some of the answers are in this annual!

1. What breed of horse do the riders at the Spanish Riding School of Vienna ride?

2. _ _ _ _ _ is very important for ponies' digestion

3. What is the name given to the only truly wild horse still alive today?

4. What is the name of the colour given to a horse that has golden body and blond mane and tail?

5. How many ribs do Arabian horses have?

6. When a horse or pony puts its ears back, what is it trying to tell you?

7. When you pick out a pony's hoof, do you go from heel to toe or toe to heel?

8. Where should you look when going over a jump?

9. Which brush do you use to get mud out of a pony's coat – a body brush or a dandy brush?

10. Where on a horse or pony do you take its pulse?

Tommy's Treble Trouble!

At team training!

When Katie and Tommy are chosen for the jumping team, Katie couldn't be happier. But, when the pair struggle in training, Katie's nerves start to get the better of her.

I'm so excited. I can't believe we're going to be in the same team!

Me neither. It's going to be great!

Come on you lot, Sarah will be here soon, and she'll go mad if we're not ready for training.

Alright, I'm nearly done.

Yeah, me too. I'm just helping Lucy.

I'm ready!

But then...

Tommy!

Oh, no. That's all we need – a team-mate who can't jump combinations.

Yeah, these jumps are easy compared to what we'll be doing on Saturday.

Lucy, you rode really well today – so just keep it up!

Thanks!

And, Katie, I want you to keep your reins short and kick like mad if you have to jump a big combination.

I'll try.

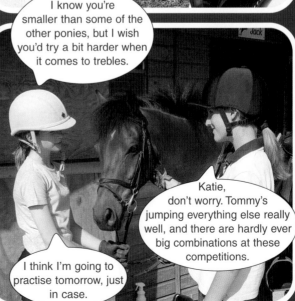

I know you're smaller than some of the other ponies, but I wish you'd try a bit harder when it comes to trebles.

Katie, don't worry. Tommy's jumping everything else really well, and there are hardly ever big combinations at these competitions.

I think I'm going to practise tomorrow, just in case.

Tam jumps clear

Katie jumps the last part clear!

The end!

fess ups! special!

We've been snooping around the PONY offices to scoop the dirt and embarrassing stories that have happened behind the scenes – and we thought we'd blurt out the truth to you! Find out what the team has to hide in our exclusive fess ups special!

When I was about two or three years old, I rode my pony in a basket saddle. It was really comfy and stopped me from wobbling off the side when I was too little to ride properly. One day, my dad took me into a lead rein class at a show. We were doing really well and my pony was called in to third place in the line up. While we waited for the other ponies to perform their shows, I fell fast asleep.

My dad tried to wake me up, but it was no good – I was fast asleep! When it was our turn, my dad had no choice but to lead me round still snoozing. When we stopped at the judge, she soon saw that I was asleep and we were moved down the line by several places! If I'd have woken up, I'd have been *sooo* embarrassed. And, worse than that, my dad's never forgiven me for doing it!

Zoe, PONY's Website Ed

Cringe-om
Snore scandal!
3

It was Saturday and, as usual, I was working on the Saturday Morning show. The studio was buzzing with excitement as all of Girls Aloud were going to be on the show to play their new single and chat with the presenters. With everything that was going on, I kind of forgot to behave. I was sitting by the girls' feet and suddenly I saw what I thought was a great dog chew. I set about chewing it, and became quite oblivious that I was on live TV. Unfortunately, it turned out not to be a chew after all. What I actually had my teeth wrapped around was one of the girls', very expensive Italian boot heels – oops!

Bruce, AKA Snowy, from the Saturday Morning show

Cringe-om
Boot bust!
2

I was about 12 years old and I was taking part in a hunter trial competition with my loan pony, Snip. We were doing really well, fast and clear. We had a great rhythm as we galloped towards a brush fence right on the brow of the hill. Snip took off, then all of a sudden we both saw that we were jumping into a field full of cows!

Snip was really spooked by the cows and darted off to the right. I, on the other hand, went to the left and we parted company. Everyone who was watching couldn't work out what had happened, it looked like I had just fallen off for no reason – which was really embarrassing and I never lived it down!

Penny, PONY's Ed Assistant

Cringe-ometer
Cow catastrophe!
4

When I was learning to ride at my local riding school, we used to have gymkhana competitions every now and then. I really wanted to win, so I was giving it everything. One of the races was the bucket and ball. I was determined not to miss the bucket so I leaned right over the side of the pony I was riding as we cantered towards the bucket.

I leant over just a little bit too far, and started to slip over the edge. Next thing I knew, I was tumbling towards the ground. Instead of getting the ball in the bucket, I landed head-first into it! I have never been so embarrassed in all my life!

Louise, PONY's Assistant Ed

Cringe-ometer
Bucket blunder!
5

Brown

Iron grey

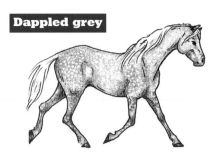
Dappled grey

Tri-coloured

Colour me
beautiful!

H orses and ponies come in a wonderful array of colour combinations. From strawberry to blue, and black to white, there are practically enough horse colours to make a rainbow! And that's not all – there are face, leg and body markings of all shapes and sizes, too!

Chestnut

Stars and Stripes!

Facial markings on ponies are made up of white hairs and have different names according to their size, shape, and position. Here's the low-down on the most common!

- A **blaze** is a wide stripe of white hair which marks the length of the face, extending over one or both nostrils.
- A **white face** is a broad white marking which extends over the pony's eye.
- A **star** is a white patch of hair between the pony's eyes.
- A **stripe** is a narrow white strip of hair which runs from the forehead towards the muzzle.
- A **snip** is a white patch of hair between the nostrils.
- A **white muzzle** is a patch of white hair which extends over both nostrils.

Lovely legs!

Leg markings can be made from black or white hairs (although most commonly white). Here's a few of the most common!

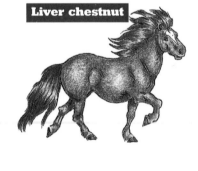
Liver chestnut

- A **stocking** is a white leg which extends over the knee or hock.
- A **sock** is a white marking to the fetlock joint.
- A **white coronet** is a thin white marking around the coronet band.
- A **white heel** is a smudge of white on the heel.
- Other white markings can be described as being white to the point of anatomy they reach. For example, **half-white cannon**.
- An **ermine mark** is a black mark on a white leg – these are usually small.
- **Zebra stripes** are often found on dun horses, they are dark, stripy marks on the leg.

Black

Piebald

Chestnut with flaxen mane

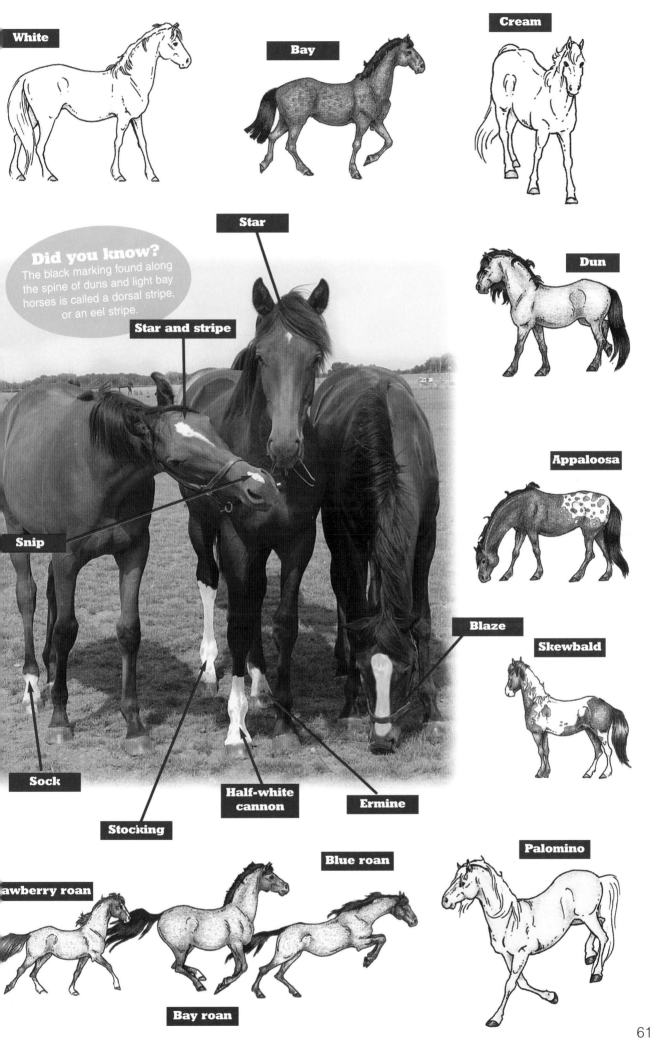

White

Bay

Cream

Star

Did you know?
The black marking found along the spine of duns and light bay horses is called a dorsal stripe, or an eel stripe.

Dun

Star and stripe

Snip

Appaloosa

Sock

Blaze

Skewbald

Half-white cannon

Ermine

Stocking

Blue roan

Palomino

awberry roan

Bay roan

Spring

In spring, your fave pony will be shedding his old coat and growing a shiny new one for the summer. Sadly, this usually results in you wearing the old one home! But the good news is that you can have lots of fun bonding with your fave pony while you massage him with a rubber curry comb and get rid of his excess winter coat!

What to watch!

● Sudden growth spurts in the grass can cause ponies to become overweight and put them at risk of laminitis. Keep a check on your fave pony's pasture to make sure he's not getting too many carbohydrates, and restrict his grazing if you're worried he's putting on weight. Spot the signs of laminitis before your pony is suffering by monitoring his weight, feeling his crest to make sure it's not too hard and making sure his coronary band (the bit at the top of his hooves) isn't hot.

● **Worms – you need to worm your pony all year round, but spring is a time when you should be particularly careful to poo-pick your fields as dung could have worm eggs in. Follow a strict worming plan all year, and make sure new horses introduced to the field have been wormed.**

Clean, re-proof and pack away your winter rugs so that they're as good as new next time you need them. And give your tack a thorough clean, taking the opportunity to check the stitching, flocking and fit of your saddle while you do it.

Why not make a list of all the horsy things you think could benefit from a spring clean, then spend 20 minutes a day to get them all done?

Summer

Summer time is show time! There are so many fab competitions going on across the summer, it's a good idea to plan your diary to make the most of your time. Keep an eye on the ground, as too much work on hard ground is really tough on your pony's legs, and work your pony on a good surface when possible.

Enjoy planning long summer rides, and remember that if you're putting sun cream on yourself, your pony may need some, too, especially if he's got pink skin.

What to watch!

● **Flies and insects can cause misery for ponies, especially if they suffer from sweet itch. Help your pony's natural bug deterrents by applying fly repellent, feeding garlic, and using a fly mask if necessary. If you spot your pony scratching and getting sores on his crest, tail, wither or rump he may be suffering from sweet itch, so call your vet for advice.**

● Some ponies suffer from dry, cracked feet in the summer. Keep daily checks of your pony's hooves and get your farrier to trim or shoe him regularly to stop cracks from widening and causing a real problem. There are supplements and creams you can use to keep your pony's hooves in top shape, but be patient as hooves grow slowly.

Looking after ponies – whatever the weather!

Autumn

If you love crisp mornings and watching the leaves change colour, there really is no better way to experience it than on horseback! Keep an eye on how hairy your fave pony gets, and if he starts to get very sweaty when you ride him, it's time to book him in for a new hair do! Make sure you think about how your pony will spend the winter months before you clip him, and whether you have warm enough rugs and a stable if you're going to choose a hunter, blanket, or full clip.

What to watch!

- **Laminitis doesn't just happen in spring** – the new grass growth in autumn means you need to watch your pony like a hawk!
- Look out for itching – mites and mange are common at this time of year. If you're worried, speak to your vet who will be able to give you advice on how to treat it.
- **Start to think about rugging and feeding your pony if the temperature drops. He will use lots of energy to keep himself warm during cold spells, so you either need to replace that energy with food, or use a rug to stop him getting cold.**

Winter

Riding in a winter wonderland is great fun, and brings its own excitement! If you love jumping, look out for indoor classes. Whether you want to be a spectator at a big show like Olympia, or take part yourself, indoor jumping is fast and furious with lots of challenging twists and turns!

What to watch!

- Keep a check on your pony's weight. If he loses too much weight at this time of year, it's hard to get him back in good condition. As always, prevention is better than cure!
- **If your pony is prone to mud fever, or has white legs, check his legs for signs of mud fever. You can use feed supplements or barrier creams to prevent it, or stable your pony for a while to keep him out of the mud.**
- The big freeze doesn't only mean you can't ride outside – water troughs can freeze and block your pony's access to the water, and snow blocks his access to the grass. Combat this by breaking the ice and providing hay or other forage for your pony to eat.
- **Listen for coughs and look out for a runny nose, which are signs of RAO (Recurrent Airway Obstruction) which is caused by dust. The extra time your pony spends in the stable during winter and increased hay rations means he's at a higher risk of suffering from RAO. If you're worried, consult your vet and look for dust-free feeds and bedding.**

back to the future!

We can trace the development of horses back to a mega-60 million years ago! It's a bit hard to imagine, but it's true! All animals, including humans and horses, have developed over many, many years, adapting to the changing environment. It is this ability to change that has enabled them to survive.

Here's the amazing story of the horse's evolution…

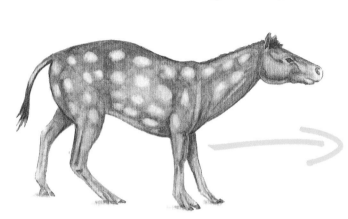

60 million years ago…

Horses of today looked very different 60 million years ago. This animal was known as Eohippus.

● Eohippus was much smaller in size (35cm or 14in) than today's horses – more like a dog or fox in size.
● **His feet had toes supported by a pad – this made it easy to move around on the soft soil they lived on.**
● He had short teeth – ideal to chew the soft leaves on the low-growing shrubs.
● **Coat markings included light spots on a darker background to provide camouflage in the forest surroundings, making it easier to hide.**

35-40 million years ago…

The next major change in horses' development came with an animal called Mesohippus. The changes were due to the physical changes in the environment in which the jungle conditions were slowly giving way to wooded, scrub areas.

● **Mesohippus was larger than Eohippus – about 45cm or 18in in height.**
● His legs were longer, enabling him to run faster, and the toes on the forefeet were reduced to just three.
● **The development of incisor teeth began, enabling Mesohippus to cope with different types of leaves and foliage.**
● The spots on the coats started to fade as the need for camouflage became less important.

The Zebra
There are three main species of zebra still alive – Grevy's Zebra (the largest of the three), Burchell's Zebra and the sleeker mountain zebra. The zebra family lives throughout southern Africa in herds.

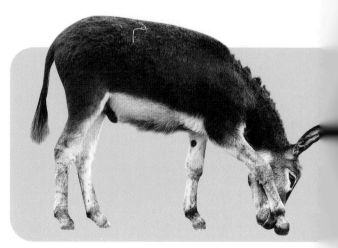

30 million years ago...

Miohippus and Parahippus emerged as slightly more advanced forms of Mesohippus.

Six million years ago...

Pliohippus looked much more like today's horse and had hooves instead of toes.

One million years ago...

Equus caballus – the name for today's horse – emerged from Pliohippus.
● Pliohippus was also the source for other members of the 'horse' family – such as zebras and asses.

20-25 million years ago...

The development to Mercyhippus was an important one in the horse's development.
● This animal was much taller – 90cm or 36in.
● Though he was still three-toed, he took most of its weight on the central toes, using the outside toes less and less. This was the beginning of the development of the hoof.
● His neck was longer, so that he could feed at ground level and higher up.
● His eyes, and the shape of his head, changed to give him more all-round vision.
● The teeth changed so that they could withstand the effect of the grinding action needed to chew grass.
● He began to develop the heightened senses which today's horses have.

2006/2007

The story doesn't quite end there as there was more development in the years after the emergence of Equus caballus. Scientists now agree that the modern, domestic horse we see today was founded in three horses which came after this:
● **The Forest Horse – thick-legged and heavy-bodied, with thick, coarse hair.**
● The Asiatic Wild Horse – also known as Przewalskii's Horse – which is the only truly wild horse still alive today. It is preserved in some zoos and some groups have recently been returned to the wild.
● **The Tarpan – lighter in build.**

Przewalskii's horse - the only truly wild horse still alive today.

The Domestic Ass

The domestic ass or donkey is related to the horse, but there are quite a few differences between them:
● Donkeys don't have chestnuts on their hindlegs
● Donkeys have five lumbar vertebrae rather than six which horses have.
● Their ears are much longer.
● Their mane is short and upright and there's no forelock.
● Their tails are tufted like a cow's

....and they make the most magnificent sound, known as a bray – not at all like horses' voices!

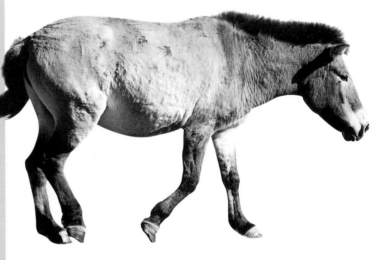

A stable yard is a place where it's important to do everything safely. Our stable yard is full of potential hazards and everyone seems to be doing everything wrong! Can you spot all the errors? And no, we haven't forgotten to give the page some colour! We've left this page so you can colour it in – and as you do so, you'll no doubt find all 30 accidents just waiting to happen.

Now turn to page 96 to find out whether you spotted all the mistakes!

Safety at the yard

Colour-in the page and find the mistakes!

What we all aspire to!

Hard to criticise my beautiful position here – or Charlotte's if she's reading this. She is looking straight ahead, she's really 'giving' with her hands and she has taken her weight off my back to make the jump as easy as it can possibly be. Look at her leg position: she keeps it from going backwards, which means she has a safe position in the saddle, and she keeps her leg on me so that I don't slow down (she knows me too well!).

For once, I am concentrating properly, and even looking ahead to the next fence. My front feet are neat and tidy and you can see that I am enjoying this jump!

GO JUMPING
with Duggie

Give me a good rider and I love jumping. It's fun, it's fast and it gives me the chance to show how strong I am. This is my guide (produced with the help of my rider, Charlotte) to what you should be thinking of when you go jumping.

Warming up...

...doesn't sound much like it has anything to do with jumping, but it is a critical part of the whole thing. Charlotte likes to warm me up to make sure that I'm listening to her aids and to make sure my muscles are all warm and stretchy before I tackle the jumps. She will also feel if there is anything wrong with me, for example if I am lame or sore, and will make sure I am going in a balanced way before she points me in the

direction of a jump – let me at 'em! You can see Charlotte's happy with me here – I'm listening to her, working from behind (apparently using my hindquarters properly is crucial for jumping), and I am pretty light in front.

The Approach

1. We can't be perfect all the time, and this shows us doing things a bit wrong as we approach the fence. I blame the photographer myself as she asked Charlotte to try leaning too far forward to see what would happen... and you can see exactly what did happen! I am completely unbalanced. My nose is coming down and I look like I am going to trip over, not jump over, the beautiful pink and purple Polyjump ahead of me. Not to be repeated!

2. And here's proof that we can approach jumps the right way! See how Charlotte is sitting up more this time, and how much this helps me to get in a balanced position as we glide towards our fence. I'm back on my hocks, ready to spring up and forwards. Go Duggie!

Smooth landing

Take-off and landing – they're both crucial phases of jumping. Here, let me tell you, I am landing well. Charlotte still has her legs forward and is not pulling with her hands like so many riders do. Her legs are still there close to me, asking me to go on to the next fence which she's looking at. My powerful hindquarters are tucked up nicely and you can tell that I am listening!

Oh, oh...

That photographer was at it again... asking Charlotte this time to sit back in the saddle and slip her reins. You can see from my face that I am not happy with what this does to my balance. I am all over the place, and not able to get my legs and body doing what they should be. A bit of a disheartening picture for both of us, but proof that small changes in a rider's position have a catastrophic effect on the pony. My ears are going back and I am about to swish my tail in annoyance at being put in this compromising position.

Big and wide!

Charlotte thinks it is important to jump wide fences so that I remember not to go just up and down, but to go up, over and down. I love a challenge like this and, for once, the photographer asked the right question when she suggested we try a larger fence. Charlotte and I are looking forward properly, she has good rein contact and I am feeling (and looking) powerful.

Know when to stop

is good to end on a positive note – and that's when you should stop your schooling session so that you always go away knowing you have achieved something.

Cross-country jumping

Yo would be entitled to think that I am unusually clever being able to jump with my eyes closed! This was the very first cross-country fence I jumped at my very first cross-country competition. Apart from having my eyes shut tightly, I'm not doing too badly.

And this was the last jump on that same course. I was totally shattered because the course was very hilly and hard work for a newcomer like me. But Charlotte was pleased that I carried on trying to the end, despite the exhaustion. And at least I am managing to keep my eyes open.

Don't cut corners!

Not all ponies love jumping as much as I do. So, if you try this tactic of coming in on a sharp angle and not jumping the fence in the middle, you are in real danger of a run-out. This picture shows how easy it would be for me to veer to the side and avoid the jump.

Duggie's do's & don'ts

- **Do** 'give' with your hands so that we are not jabbed in the mouth as we go over the jump
- **Don't** let the reins go so long that we fall on our noses!
- **Do** keep your leg on and in a strong position – it shouldn't fall backwards
- **Do** fold forwards over the jump so that your weight is off our backs, but don't forget to sit up after the jump or you'll fall off!
- **Do** sit up before the jump so we are well-balanced in readiness for take-off
- **Don't** forget to look ahead at all times – if you look down, that's where you will end up!

Stallion of the Storm

By PONY reader Maddie Pitt

PONY Magazine short story competition finalist

The only horse on the yard that I had been expressly forbidden to ride was Colorado. He was a truly awe-inspiring chestnut stallion of 15hh. I had seen photographs of him ridden by my instructor, Samantha, flying over three-feet wide solid tree trunks, and charging with fearless courage through water jumps, looking powerful and muscular. Colorado was really a horse to admire, and I admired him! I could recall the excitement when, almost 11 months ago, Sam's mare Dreamer had been put in foal – Colorado was going to be a dad!

One unbearably hot and humid day in late August, I arrived early at the stables to see the last of the four liveries being loaded into the horse box. I don't have my own pony, but often help out and get rides on the ponies kept there.

"What's happening?" I asked one of the girls.

"Pony Club Camp," she answered excitedly. "See you next week!"

Rather jealously, I waved them off, thinking that I would have no riding for a week, for there were no other horses on the yard but the mare and Colorado. Then I heard Sam's excited voice call from one of the stables.

"Lizzie, she called, "I think Dreamer's going to foal today!"

I rushed over to the stable, feeling my heart leap with excitement. The beautiful grey mare was lying down and looking agitated, tossing her head and sweating in a deep bed of straw. Anxiously, we watched her until I had to go home.

I had promised to help Dad in the garage, so I spent a frustrating day glancing out of the window every few seconds into the fiery, sizzling heat, wondering if Dreamer had foaled yet, whether it would be a colt or a filly, and what colour the young, fluffy coat would be. Trying to imagine a frisky colt galloping round the field, finding his feet and exploring the world, I accidentally stepped on a cardboard box and squashed it, which Dad wasn't exactly delighted with. I felt so impatient to be kept in; I wanted to be part of the excitement at the stables and, as soon as I was released, I seized my bike and

> **"Lizzie, she called, "I think Dreamer's going to foal today!"**

> **The mare was lying down and looking agitated**

set off, pedalling frantically.

It happened very quickly; the heat broke, the sky darkened and heavy, pounding rain began to fall. Fearsome black thunderclouds billowed across the sky. I arrived at the stables five minutes later, gasping for breath and soaked to the skin, as a fork of lightning illuminated the landscape temporarily before it was engulfed into blackness once more, and a terrifying crash of thunder seemed to shake the very axis of the earth. The noise of rain lashing onto the roof of the stables was frightening, it was so loud. Tearing over to Dreamer's stable, I held my breath and looked inside.

Nothing could have prepared me for what I was to see; Sam was crying as she struggled to hold the mare, who was spinning on the spot in a state of terror. Sweat dripped from her flanks, and blood flowed in streams from her hock. Her eyes were wild, rolling and fearful. My heart plummeted.

"Lizzie!" Sam yelled above the crashing of the rain, "the telephone lines have been pulled down and there's no signal from my mobile. There's no one else here... get the vet..."

This was no time to protest or argue against it; Dreamer was going to kill not only herself, but the unborn foal as well. If one of her thrashing hooves struck Sam... But Phillip Jones the vet lived miles away over the moors with not a house for miles, and my bike would have no chance against the rough quagmires the moor possessed. I couldn't do anything but run. Then I realised...Colorado!

The rest of the horses were at camp and it seemed he was the only hope if Dreamer and his foal were to survive. My danger in embarking on this wild cross-country ride was irrelevant. I had to do everything I could to save Dreamer.

Without a second thought, I sprinted through the rain to the shed and ripped Colorado's saddle and bridle from its stand. Cramming my riding hat on, I staggered to the stallion's stable and flung open the door. For the first time I

didn't think how tall and strong, even intimidating, Colorado looked. It was as though we were working as a team together, as equals. Within seconds, the saddle was on his back and, reaching above my head, I slipped the thick snaffle between his teeth. My fingers fumbled with haste as I buckled the throatlash and girth, because I knew that every second counted. I could almost see the clock before my eyes, ticking with gathering, merciless speed. The lashing and the drumming of the rain went on overhead.

Suddenly, there was nothing more to be done. This is it, I thought, as my heart hammered as fiercely and relentlessly as the rain. Jogging alongside Colorado, he spun round in anticipation and somehow, I landed my foot in the hovering stirrup, grasped hold of the pommel and swung myself up. Colorado gave a half-rear and tugged at the bit as soon as I was in the saddle. He felt so powerful and wide compared to the other ponies, even though he was only inches higher, but I had no time to think about it.

My heels barely touched his sides as he reared in the air, surging straight into a canter in the yard, towards the road that led to the moor, his hooves clattering and splashing in a regular rhythm on the concrete. Never had I felt such power and impulsion underneath me – the difference mus

> **My fingers fumbled with haste as I buckled the throatlash and girth, because I knew that every second counted**

be like that between a Fiesta and a Ferrari. As we passed by the stable, I saw Dreamer rear again, her head missing the stable roof by a hair's breadth as she fell.

Hurry!

Out of the yard, onto the mud track, faced with a three-foot hedge, a short cu to the moors. Without even thinking, I turned Colorado towards it; he bounded forward and felt a sudden surge of confidence and trust as he took a huge, powerful leap and cleared it by feet. The moment we landed, I felt his muscles bunch and he began to stretch out into flat-out gallop across the darkened, deserted landscape. Slashing rain cut into my face like an avalanche of white-hot knives. Knowing that under normal circumstances this was one of the thing

Faster and faster flew Colorado, faster than a racing car, faster than the wind...

would never do, I leaned forward like a jockey and urged him on. Faster and faster he flew, faster than a racing car, faster than the wind that howled through the hills and whistled in my ears. Chunks of mud soared up behind us, and another bolt of lightning flashed across the sky. Thunder boomed like the very clap of God, and it became suddenly clear in my own mind that no rules applied to this horse. There was no-one to stop me and, equally, no-one to help me. I'd have to handle this alone.

Colorado's coat was dark with sweat and rain, almost black. His mane lay flattened and drenched along the crest of his neck. The reins were slippery and difficult to grip. Was Dreamer still alive...?

"She has to be," I thought despairingly. "She must be!"

Suddenly, I saw a light in the distance; yellow, welcoming, warm, yet taunting me, mocking me, retreating further and further away. It *must* be the vet's house... but if it wasn't, all would be lost.

Colorado was tiring and slowing to a rough, staggering canter. Mud had splattered his chest as densely as it had covered my jodhpurs, and I could feel the dampness soaking through. Frantically I urged Colorado on, but he couldn't keep the pace and he slowed to a jagged trot, and finally a walk, breathing hard and fast in noisy gasps.

"I'm sorry," I told him, suddenly realising what he had been through. "I know you don't understand." Patting him, the thought blasted through my head: '*Every second counts, and every second means Dreamer is thrashing around her stable.*'

Minutes passed and the stallion recovered his breath. I shivered in the raging storm as I roused Colorado into a trot and then a canter once more. Approaching a stone wall, we met it on a perfect stride and Colorado hauled

I rested my head against Colorado's strong shoulder for a moment, before taking his reins and starting the long walk home

himself over, tired but still fighting. The light was near and with another flash of lightning, I could make out a pebble-dashed cottage and a garden.

Relief flooded through me as I threw myself off Colorado and ran, stumbling, to the house.

"*Phillip!*" I yelled above the storm, hammering the door with my fists as water cascaded down. "Phillip!"

"Oh no, I thought," my heart sinking in bitter disappointment, "he's not in. *What do I do now?*"

Suddenly, there were swift footsteps and the door was pulled open. There, in the hallway, stood the man I most wanted to see in the whole world.

"Phillip," I choked, "It's Dreamer..." and I explained in a rush of tears and relief about the mare. Phillip seized his bag and folded himself behind the wheel of his van, pausing with the door ajar to stare at me.

"Wait a minute..." he said, slowly, "...you rode...?"

"Just go, it's an emergency!" I cried in desperation, gesturing him away. "I'll be all right, I'll see you back at the yard. Please hurry!"

I watched his van rocket down the twisting lanes to the moors. Glancing at the sky, I saw it was no longer an unbroken, jet black, but a gentle softening blue as the thunderclouds surrendered to the sun. I felt empty now that my part had been played, and I could do no more to help. I rested my head against Colorado's strong shoulder for a moment, before taking his reins and starting the long walk home.

Two hours later, we clattered into the yard in the gentle sunlight of a late summer evening. The birds were singing softly in the hedgerows, and the fallen rain shone and glistened on the grass.

Stopping outside Colorado's stable, I slid off his saddle. His dark eyes were calm and trusting as he looked at me. I was so grateful to him, but I was yet to know whether our ride had done any good. I threw on his cooler rug, filled him a hay net and left him munching.

Slowly, I walked across the deserted yard, hearing voices in the end stable but not being able to hear the exact words. I was dreading what was to come, but I had to know whether I had been too late. I stopped outside Dreamer's stable and took a deep breath – what had happened?

Phillip leaned over the stable door. He was smiling.

"Look what you've done, Lizzie," he said to me.

Inside the stable, stumbling around the happy mare in the straw, with an uneven fluffy mane and tail, on gangling legs with a soft pink muzzle, was a tiny chestnut foal. Colorado's foal.

Big is beaut

Horses with serious pulling power!

The Shire horse is the old fashioned equivalent of a pick-up truck. They're powerful off-roaders which can pull just about anything over any terrain. Find out how they came to be, what we used them for, and where you can see them today!

Fact file
Height: Over 17hh
Colour: Black, brown, bay and grey
Weight: Over a tonne
Temperament: Docile, gentle horses
Characteristics: Big-bodied horses with relatively long necks, big round feet, heavy straight feather and broad flat hocks.
Ideal for: Pulling heavy loads over rugged terrain.

Did you know?
The girth of a shire horse varies between six and eight feet (1.8-2.4m)!

Did you know?
The measurement around the cannon bone of a Shire horse is 11-12 inches (28-36cm)!

Shires make great driving horses!

ful

Origins

Shire horses are a British native breed, originally bred in Leicestershire, Staffordshire, Derbyshire and the Fen country of Lincolnshire. The Shire is a descendent of the English Great Horse which knights rode into battle in the 16th century. Evidence suggests that the English Great Horse was a heavy cob type, measuring around 15.2hh – a midget compared to today's Shires!

At the end of the 16th century, the English Great Horse was used less for riding, and more to pull heavy carts. So when Flanders horses and Friesians were imported to help drain the Fens, they were bred with the English Great Horse to produce a horse more suitable for the heavy, agricultural, work horses then carried out. At this point, the English horses used for draught work became known as English Blacks.

The first horse to be referred to as a Shire horse was the Packington Blind Horse, who stood at stud in the mid 18th century. A large number of horses were sired by this big black horse, and in 1876 the English Cart Horse Society was formed to regulate the breeding of the Shire horse. The society soon changed its name to the Shire Horse Society and in its heyday, 5000 horses were registered each year!

> **Did you know?**
> One pair of Shires used to pull against a dynamometer (an instrument for measuring force) were estimated to pull a load the equivalent to 50 tonnes!

In the 16th century, knights rode an ancestor of the Shire!

Traditions

The Shire Horse was a very important part of society in the early 20th century. They were used to pull heavy carts carrying goods over long distances, and they were the farming equivalent of the tractor, being used to pull ploughs across large fields. Many were exported to America to be used for industry and agriculture there, too.

However, the Second World War brought on a sudden decline in the role of the Shire, and therefore in the popularity of breeding them. Horses had been replaced by modern vehicles and there was no going back for the Shire.

Shires today!

Modern Shires owe much of their success to beer – no really! Breweries traditionally used Shire horses to pull vehicles called drays which delivered beer to pubs. Whilst most beer is now transported by lorries or other means, many breweries maintain a display team of Shires, and until recently the Young's brewery in Wandsworth, London, used Shires to deliver their ale within a two mile radius of the plant!

Many Shire enthusiasts have also diversified – turning their hand to riding Shires, and you can even see jousting Shires in action!

Imagine riding a Shire!

> **Did you know?**
> A Shire horse weighs the equivalent of four Colonels!*

> **Did you know?**
> There are usually around 300 Shires on show at the annual Shire Horse Show in Peterborough – check out www.shire-horse.org.uk to find out how you can see them!

*Colonel the pony, not army Colonels!

If you're **100% pony mad**, you'd be **mad to miss** PONY **Mag**!

PONY **Mag** is crammed full of...

- **Riding features**
- Pony care advice and tips
- **Readers' real life experiences**
- Top tips from celeb riders
- **Readers letters, ponies, pets**
- Charlie's PONY **Mag** Club page
- **News on Duggie and Colonel!**
- Lots of competitions to win and giveaways to send for!

PONY is published every four weeks – place an order with your newsagent or subscribe today so you don't miss a single issue!

For more info about PONY **Magazine** log on to www.ponymag.com

Charlie gets horse power!

So, Charlie – what do you want for your birthday?

I'm not sure. Why, are you actually going to buy me a present this year? Ha ha.

Mum, I've had a fab idea for Charlie's birthday!

What's that, dear? A nice knitted jumper?

No, some motorbike lessons! He really wants a bike, so we could help start him off!

It's Charlie's birthday...

As usual, hardly any presents. Humph.

What's that?

Who knows? You'd better go and see!

BEEP BEEP!

Hop on the bike – this is your first lesson!

Really? How cool!

Happy birthday, Charlie!

This is the best birthday ever!

Charlie, you're doing really well!

This is even better than I thought it'd be!

The lesson was awesome!

There's more – we've booked you a whole course of lessons, and the test, too!

Wow, cool!

We're going to practise overtaking now.

Bye Mum, we're going to get some leathers and look at a bike, too!

Okay, but be careful!

Those are posh leathers, Charlie!

I know, so I got a secondhand bike, but it'll do for now!

So long as it's safe, Charlie...

Now just remember everything you've learnt.

Yes Mum, I know! I'm just really nervous!

Look, Mum – no L plates!

Well done Charlie, I knew you could do it!

Ooh – look at that hunk on that motorbike!

Wow – the girls love me!

See ya Charlie!

Huh?!

SPLITT!

HOLEE-06

75

Backstage at White Rocks Farm!

If you log in to ponymag.com, you'll know about animal trainer Sue Woods, from White Rocks Farm, who posts her blog of what's happening online. And, if you haven't been reading the *adventures in animal training* – it's time you met the gang!

Sue Woods trains and breeds Western horses, and just about every other animal you can imagine. She uses a variety of methods to make training interesting for all the animals she works with, so that when they are working it feels more like they're just having fun! Many of Sue's animals have TV careers, but however famous they become, none of the animals are allowed to act like divas!

Sue encourages the young people who help out at the farm to get involved with the animals. When we went behind the scenes, young handler Marley showed us how to join-up with a pony under Sue's watchful eye!

Come together

Join-up is a method Sue uses with all the horses at the farm (and there are a few). It's used by horse trainers like Kelly Marks and Monty Roberts to back and train horses naturally – without using force. Join-up should only be done in a round pen, like the one Marley uses, and with the supervision of someone who knows what they're doing, like Sue. Here, we see the stages of join-up as Marley forms a bond with Shetland cross, Sprout.

Stage 1

Marley sends Sprout away from him. He has to use his body language to look big and imposing to Sprout – just like a dominant horse in a herd would. Sprout responds by cantering around the pen – showing the natural flight instinct of the horse.

While Sprout is cantering, Marley has to watch for signs that Sprout is listening to him. He looks for whether Sprout's ears are pointing forwards, or if they're in the side position – which shows his attention is on Marley. He watches Sprout's mouth to see if he is licking and chewing – a sign that Sprout is telling him that he's listening and that he's submissive to Marley.

Stage 2

When Marley is happy that all of Sprout's attention is on him all of the time, he stops sending Sprout away. Instead, Marley simply stops and turns his eyes away from Sprout. Marley looks to the floor and makes his body language very passive so that he no longer looks like a threat to Sprout.

Sprout sees the change in Marley's body language and almost immediately stops in his tracks, watching Marley all the time. Now, Marley has to carefully sneak a look at Sprout from the corner of his eye. He checks to see that Sprout is still watching him, but must be very careful not to look Sprout in the eye.

Stage 4

Once Marley's at Sprout's side, he is still careful not to look him in the eye, but he gives Sprout a scratch on the head so that they can become friends.

Stage 5

As Marley walks away, Sprout follows his new friend wherever he goes – we hope Marley doesn't mind having a four-legged stalker!

It's a natural thing

You'd be mistaken for thinking Sprout was just fighting with Tiny, the Shetland, when actually he's learning lots of social skills. Sprout and Tiny are around the same age, and they use play fighting to learn how to communicate with other horses, and where they fit into the pecking order of the herd. Young horses must learn to do this so that they can become well-rounded individuals with all the skills necessary to fit into herd life. All of Sue's horses grow up with other youngsters in a herd situation, so that they can learn to be horses.

Stage 3

When Marley knows Sprout's still watching him, he very slowly walks towards Sprout, keeping his eyes down and his body language passive. You can see how intently Sprout watches everything Marley does, and at this stage one sudden move, or aggressive look from Marley would send Sprout away again.

Star spotting!

If you thought the animals at White Rocks were ordinary cats and dogs – you'd be very much mistaken! Here's a few of our fave performing stars enjoying their time away from the cameras.

Andy the pig loves wallowing in mud when he's not busy appearing in the Basil Brush show!

This cute cat was one of six cats who played the part of the silver tabby in Harry Potter!

Bruce (AKA Snowy) has finished appearing on the Saturday Morning Show for the summer, and as you can see, he just loves having a cuddle from Sue!

Sandy the jumping goat is just waiting for his TV debut – but he's still a star in our eyes, so couldn't miss appearing in the PONY Annual!

Don't try this at home!

Mini mayhem!

We couldn't give you a guided tour of White Rocks without checking out the progress of our fave miniature foals – after all, PONY readers named two of this tiny trio. We're glad to report that Popcorn, Giggle and Doodlebug are all thriving! They were all most intrigued to find out what Marley was doing on the floor so came over to have a good look!

Colonel's Cunning Plan...

So what's his great plan of yours then?

We need to get the dogs here.

They're probably sleeping indoors – as usual!

There's a dog-flap in the kitchen door, so call them!

What's up? We were having a nap.

It's an emergency – there's a burglar in the yard.

Can you do something?

A burglar? Could he be dangerous?

Don't be such a wuss.

Well, you have to be careful.

Suddenly, the burglar burst out of the yard, the dogs in hot pursuit.

How dare you!

Yes, go away, nasty man!

And don't come back, or else!

The burglar didn't stop running – and the dogs chased him to the end of the drive.

Duggie, Soloman and Colonel have spotted a would-be burglar approaching the stable yard. Everyone is out, but Colonel has a cunning plan...

PART 2

Soloman whinnied.

Ouch... that's a bit loud.

The two dogs, Specs and Gypsy, were soon on the scene.

For goodness sake, he's going to take the tack!

Don't worry, we've got it sorted!

The dogs sped away to the yard. The ponies waited in anticipation. Everything went very quiet.

Well Colonel, you've saved the day with your cunning plan.

I'm a bit busy right now. Call me if anything else happens...

Yes, burglars beware. Where is Colonel, anyway?

THE END

🔊 **A Duggie, Colonel and Soloman production**

Cast: Duggie, Colonel, Soloman, Specs and Gypsy as themselves. G.O.D as the burglar. Shot on location on Marley Common. Striped top, mask and swag bag all model's own. Look out for *Colonel's Cunning Plan* merchandise in stores near you.

Make a horsy

How to do it!

1 With the ruler, mark the centre of one piece of card (26cms), then mark a centimetre either side of this. Do this on both sides of the card.

2 Glue the edges of one piece of card.

3 Carefully stick the other piece of card to the glued card.

6 This provides you with room to put your horsy stuff!

4 Carefully score a line from one of the marks either side of the centre mark to the other, and do the same with the second marks.

5 Fold this scored line, using the ruler.

7 With the ruler, make a mark 15cms from the top of the card. Make another 15cm from the other end of the card. Make another mark along the bottom edge, 12 cms from the end, and another along the top edge, 12cms from the end.

8 Carefully punch holes where the marks are. You can do this easily if you take the back off the hole punch, so you can see where you are punching!

folder

Here's a fab way to store horsy stuff and carry to and from school or the yard. You can decorate it any way you choose – we pinched a couple of PONY posters to make ours look particularly snazzy!

Your folder should now look like this!

9

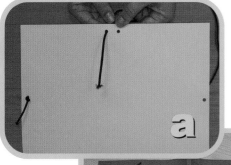

a

11

b

10

Carefully cut out the PONY posters, or pictures of your fave pony. You may prefer to draw or paint your own picture! Glue these to the outside of your folder.

Now take the elastic and thread it through the holes. Tie a knot in the end, remembering to do this on the inside of the folder. It should look like pic **a** on the inside, and pic **b** on the back of the outside. Make certain it is tight enough to lie flat on the folder.

12

The elastic folds over the front of the folder to keep all your horsy stuff in place!

You can experiment with different coloured card, and a variety of images on the outside of your folder. Why not make one as a present for a friend? You could even make a one with images of food on the outside for your mum to keep her recipes in!

Ben Maher on Mercurius!

Before you go...

Arrive at the venue in plenty of time and walk the course so you know exactly where you are going! Take notice of the best ground to take off and land, any tricky fences you might like to tackle carefully, or boldly, and any places where you may be able to make up time.

It's nearly your turn!

Warm up your pony quietly and sensibly so that he is ready to go when you are due to start. You want your pony going forward to your leg aids, but listening to you. Aim to get to the start just as you are ready to go!

The first fence

The first fence can make or break a round and sets you up for the rest of the course. It will be an inviting jump so aim for the very centre, and push on during the last three strides, so your pony knows you mean business. Once you're over, give him a pat and look towards your next jump; you're on your way!

The start

Start as you mean to go on! Go through the start when it's your turn, and ease into a steady canter. No leaping off at a gallop, or standing still so your pony doesn't want to leave his friends in the collecting ring.

Successful Cros

Drop jumps

Tackle these slowly – you can ask your pony to trot down them if you like. Keep your weight in your heels and your shoulders back and don't forget to ride straight.

Ditches

Ponies don't usually mind these jumps, but riders can be spooked by them! Look up, not in the ditch, and ride on to the horizon. You'll be over it in no time!

Take care when jumping into and out of shaded areas!

Wooded areas

Jumps which are on the edge of woods make your pony jump from light to dark areas, and then back from dark to light again. This means he may find it tricky to see clearly for a few seconds after jumping, so slow down and take a breather to let his eyes adjust to the light.

Arrowheads

These are narrow jumps, so keep your legs on so your pony can't run out, and believe you'll sail over.

The finish

As you near the finish, take into account how your pony is feeling. If he is full of running and keen to keep going, then you can push on a little. If he is struggling, then ease off and let him canter slowly. There is always another competition, another time.

As you ride through the finish line, don't pull your pony up too quickly as this could jar his legs. Do it gradually, and walk him around on foot until he has stopped blowing. Rug him up to keep his muscles warm – and tell him how fab he is!

Country

Remember

Each jump has two flags – red on the right and white on the left. You must go between the flags for the jump to count. If you don't you will get faults!

83

KNOW YOUR

Tackle our fiendishly difficult quiz to test your knowledge of the world's top horses. We've hidden all the answers in the wordsearch, so if you're not sure of an answer, get looking! Once you've answered all the questions, you can check the answers on page 98 to see how well you've done!

1
What was the name of the smallest horse ever to win the Hickstead Derby?

A. _____

3
Emma Hindle was the highest placed British dressage rider in the 2006 World Equestrian Games, but who was she riding?

A. _____

4
Which was the first horse, outside of racing, to win over a million pounds in prize money?

A. _____

2
What is the name of the horse which Leslie Law rode to Olympic Gold in Athens?

A. _____

5
On which horse did Ben Maher win the 2005 Hickstead Derby?

A. _____

6
Which heavyweight cob won the *Cob of the Year* title six times?

A. _____

7
Which of the following was not the name of a top event horse ridden by Mary King?
King William
King Boris
King Solomon
King Henry

A. _____

HORSES!

```
w n s u d p j r i l r f e
m m r p r b a l f r e d o
y o v w l e m i a n i e h
n o t l i m t r d r r t r
n n m e l n e u p e l r u
i f h a c l f s u m o e a
s l n t l n e u k y c p e
r e o o k r a e r h a u l
b e r c o e h l a t r s r
x t a m a r i l l o n b e
s a i e h d r t m w o o e
y r n e h g n i k t g r h
p t k c o r e m e r p u s
```

HOW DID YOU DO?

UNDER 6
Ooops! We think you need to open your eyes and keep up-to-date with what's going on in the world of horses!

6-8
Well done, you seem to have a good idea about who's done what – keep up the good work!

OVER 8
Congratulations! Top marks for you show that you're one top horsy bod! You know all about the top horses and their riders – well done!

Pippa Funnell won the Rolex Grand Slam in 2003 by winning Badminton, Burghley and Kentucky, but which horse was she riding when she won Badminton that year?

A. _____

John Whitaker won the 2004 Hickstead Derby on Buddy Bunn, but which horse did Ellen Whitaker ride to finish in second place?

A. _____

Who did Andrew Hoy ride when he won Badminton Horse trials for the first time?

A. _____

Name the horse William Fox-Pitt rode in both the 2004 Olympics and the 2006 World Equestrian games.

A. _____

Name the horse Ruth Edge rode when she won the British Open Championship in 2004.

A. _____

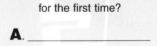

Meet the Dancing

– of the Spanish Riding School of Vienna

The history

Established in 1572, the Spanish Riding School is the oldest riding academy in the world. It's purpose was to train the Austrian nobility in equestrianism, skills which were essential at that time.

In the 16th century, the school was not nearly as grand as it is today. It started life as an outdoor wooden arena next to the imperial Palace. Then in 1729, the Emperor Charles IV commissioned the *Winter Riding Hall*, which is the hugely impressive arena still used today.

The *Winter Riding Hall* was completed in 1735 and formed part of the Hofburg Place. The Spanish Riding School is now privately owned and opens its doors to the public for gala performances.

Did you know?
Although only white horses are used for breeding at Piber, there are a few bay horses born. And, traditionally, the school always has one bay horse.

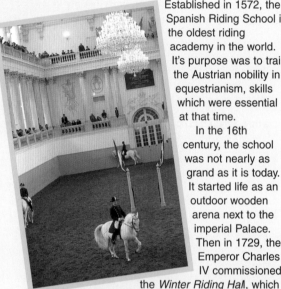

The Riders

All riders at the Spanish Riding School are Austrian citizens. It takes four to six years for a rider to reach the level considered by the school to be good enough to ride a schooled horse. Riders must then train for a further two to four years before they are considered capable of training a horse – that's a lot of training!

Riders join the school at the age of 16 and spend six months working in the stables and having a half-an-hour lunge lesson with no reins. Then riders spend about two years having lunge lessons every day with no stirrups and no reins, they practise vaulting and strengthening and loosening exercises – having their position corrected all the time – no wonder they're all brilliant riders!

The low-down on Lipizzaners

Height: 15hh – 16.1hh
Colour: Mostly white, but bay, brown and black do occur.
Type: A compact horse with strong hindquarters, good bone, an short neck. They are slow to develop, but are very hardy. Many work into their 20s and some into their 30s! They make good rid horses, but are also ideal for carriage driving and some still perf general farm work.
Character: Intelligent and very trainable, without losing charact

White Horses

The Spanish Riding School is the world's oldest and most respected riding establishment. It's got history, style, finesse and a unique breeding programme, so read on to discover the origins of the school that brought us dancing white horses!

The Horses

The Spanish Riding School trains only Lipizzaner stallions, which are bred at the stud in Piber. Every year, eight to 10 Stallions are selected for the school and start their journey of training which lasts at least four years. By the end of this initial training period, the horse will be able to perform piaffe and passage, flying changes at every stride, and pirouettes, and at this point they are assessed for their ability to progress to learning the famous *airs above the ground*.

Did you know?
The Spanish Riding School is in Austria – not Spain. It get its name from the Spanish horses which were imported to breed from.

The Leaps

There are three airs above the ground movements which are still performed by the Spanish Riding School. The first is the *levade* which involves lifting the forehand and lowering the hocks to just 20-25 cm from the ground. The horse must be able to hold this position for a short period with the front legs bent so they are tucked in.

Did you know?
The Capriole means *leap of the goat.*

The courbette

The *courbette* is a natural progression from the levade. From the position held in the levade, the horse must spring forward on this hind legs, keeping his front legs in the bent position. The final leap, and also the most demanding, is the *capriole*. It is a progression from the *courbette*, but when the horse leaps forward from the levade position, he must strike out with his hind legs so that he is propelled forward, keeping the front legs bent so that he appears to be suspended in mid air (see main pic).

zzaners are founded from Spanish horses imported to Lipizza stud, in Slovinia, which was founded in 1580. ginally, nine stallions and 24 mares were imported, in time these were bred with Italian, German and ish horses which all had Spanish influences, and an b Stallion, called Siglavvy, who became one of the six ndation stallions for the Lipizzaner breed. hese six stallion lines still exist today, and at Piber e stud of the Spanish Riding School) 14 of the original e lines exist, too.

The Old Mine

By PONY reader Hannah Baker

PONY Magazine short story competition finalist

13-year-old Jo loved horses – they had been her favourite animal all her life. Her great-grandad had worked in the mines with his faithful roan pony, Strawberry. They had worked the mine together, until a terrible accident occurred...

"So can we go Mum? Beth wants to come as well. Go on, please!" Jo implored. Beth was Jo's best friend. They each owned a pony and shared a field, so they could split the cost.

"Oh, alright, but only if you two stop irritating me," Jo's mum finally agreed.

"YES!" Jo and Beth said, as one.

"I can't believe we're actually going to see the mine my great-grandad worked in," said Jo, joyously.

"Yeah," agreed Beth. People say it's haunted."

"There are only tours twice a year. The mine is closed now."

"Well, my great-grandad died down there years ago. His friend saw it all. I wish great-grandad were still alive now," Jo said as she remembered all the things her mum had described.

"Mum said her grandad used to play with her a lot and buy her whatever she wanted. He used to read the stories she'd made up, and was a great man to know. She was in tears when they told her the news." For the rest of the day, Jo and Beth planned their trip down to every last detail.

The next day, a cockerel crowed somewhere in the mist, hastening the girls.

"Come on, it's six o'clock. We've got to groom and saddle Caramel and Bramble!" Caramel was Jo's cheeky palomino who lived for food. It was a windy day, so Jo plaited his long mane, to keep it out of his eyes. Bramble was Beth's horse, a 15.2hh dappled grey. She had a short, fluffy mane and was more cheeky than Caramel. Bramble liked to pinch snacks out of Beth's pocket.

"How are you getting on?" asked Beth impatiently.

"Okay. I'll be ready in a few minutes. It's just... he won't breath in, so I can't do up his girth. Ah! Finally!" Jo heaved a sigh of relief. At eight o'clock they were ready to set off on their journey.

A sapphire blue sky was overhead and the sun looked down on the riders from the sky. Green trees towered above them, creating a shady tunnel. Baby birds sat snugly in their nests, while their parents worked hard to provide them with meals of worms and caterpillars. The flies were irritating Bramble and Caramel, so the girls stopped for a moment to swat as many as they could. They trotted for a while in a field, but soon started cantering. A fallen log lay in their path, so they each took it in turn to jump it. Once they had cleared the log, they cantered until they came to a small country lane and, walking again, they followed the road to the outskirts of a small village. The village where the mine was.

A tour group was peparing to enter the dim darkness of the mine when the girls rode up.

"You're just in time for the tour," said a guide, and the girls quickly tied up their two ponies in the shade and joined the waiting group.

It was very cold in the mine, despite the outside temperature, and it was dark. The only light came from the battery-driven torches the guide had given everyone. Slowly, the girls crept to the back of the group.

"This is boring," Beth whispered to Jo.

"Shhhh!" Jo snapped.

"Why? It's just a mine."

"Yes, but we need to sneak off, away from the group. Now!"

Jo and Beth watched the group disappear into the distance, leaving them in the darkness.

"Where are we?" asked Beth.

"Let's see," said Jo, pulling out an old, battered map.

"Where did you get that?" asked Beth.

"It was one of my great-grandad's maps he had when he worked here with Strawberry. He passed it on to my grandad on his thirteenth birthday." Jo remembered what her mum had told her. "My mum got the map when she turned 13, and now I'm that age, I have it. I'll pass it on when my kids are thirteen."

"Wow!" said Beth, admiringly. They both looked at the map.

"What's that cross written on it for?" Beth asked.

"That's where the accident happened, and it's where we're heading," replied Jo.

After walking for ages, Beth began to moan to Jo.

"Can't we turn back? My feet are hurting and it's freezing down here!"

"Stop complaining Beth. Besides, I

think we're here."

"Are you absolutely sure? I thought there would be a pile of rocks, or something," said Beth.

"It must have been cleared away," said Jo.

Suddenly, the ground began to shake and a massive gust of wind rushed past

> **Then, a loud whinny echoed eerily along the tunnel...**

> **Beth stretched out to stroke the pony, but all she could feel was cold, damp air**

them, knocking them next to the hard, dry walls. Then, a loud whinny echoed eerily along the tunnel.

"What on earth was that?" asked Beth, close to panic.

"I don't know, Jo replied, "but it's getting closer!" Both girls shut their eyes in terror. The sound of hooves got louder and louder, faster and faster until, suddenly, all was quiet. Both girls felt breath on their cold, bare arms and slowly, they opened their eyes. There was nothing there. They looked at each other, then blinked, then looked back to where the noise had come from. A pony's face stared back at them. A pit pony in harness with blinkers on the bridle.

"That entire part of the mine collapsed. Great-grandad died, and Strawberry went with him."

could two people hallucinate the same thing, at the same time? As neither Jo, nor Beth, could feel the pony, they were shocked to see something which didn't appear to be there.

The pony stepped backwards, then it ran towards them. This time, something was different; now, they were able to feel the pony pushing them – and it was strong.

The girls looked at each other, amazed and bewildered. The pony stopped, and Jo could see the fear in its eyes. The ground shook, and small stones fell from the walls and roof. Jo and Beth got the hint; they turned and ran. They ran and ran until they thought

no evidence of any pony ever having been there.

Suddenly, Beth found something. It was a skull, a skull of a pony. Old, dry and dusty, it was years old.

"How exactly did your great-grandad die?" Beth asked, shakily.

"Strawberry started acting really weird. Great-grandad ignored him, and he offered to take the last lot of coal up to the top."

"Doesn't that mean he was safe?" asked Beth, confused.

"Let me finish!" insisted Jo. "First, of course, he had to go down and collect the coal. Strawberry refused to go, so my great-grandad took his bridle to lead him down the low, thin tunnel. A few seconds later, that entire part of the mine collapsed. Great-grandad died, and Strawberry went with him." Jo wiped away a tear, but managed to hold back the rest as she thought of what happened on that horrible day.

The girls hurried back along the dark passageway to re-join the tour group. Dirty and dazed, Jo and Beth were glad to walk out of the mine. The girls hugged their ponies. They felt warm and solid, just as they should.

As they mounted and set off for home, Beth put into words what

A pony's face stared back at them. A pit pony in harness with blinkers on the bridle.

Beth stretched out her hand to stroke the pony, but all she could feel was cold, damp air. She jumped back. Both girls were speechless. Agitated, the pony kept looking behind it, then back to them. It whinnied again, tossing his head and pawing the ground. Another rumble shook the ground and the girls wondered whether they were hallucinating, but

they were safe, and until they could run no more, then they stopped and turned around. Behind them, they could see the small pony just standing there as rocks and boulders covered it. The pony didn't even whinny. Everything went quiet and the girls carefully retraced their steps, spending ages moving rocks, hoping to find the pony's body. There was nothing,

they had both been thinking, but didn't dare ponder, something that Jo would remember for the rest of her life.

"You know that was your great-grandad's dear old pony Strawberry we saw in the mine, don't you? Or, rather, it was the ghost of Strawberry. He couldn't save your great-grandad on that terrible day, but he saved us."

Foal-fest!

What could be more irresistable than a gorgeous, cuddly foal? Nothing! Here are some ahhhh-factor pictures of cute foals, and some foal-fest facts to amaze your friends!

How long?
The gestation period for a horse or pony mare is 11 months. This is how long it takes for the foal to grow inside the mare.

The name game
A foal is so called until it is old enough to leave its mother. Usually, this is after six months, but it can vary. Then it is called a *weanling*. It then goes through being a *yearling* (one-year-old!), a *two-year-old* and a *three-year-old*.

Timing is everything
Most foals are born in the spring. This is the ideal time for a growing foal to thrive – the spring grass will ensure its dam can make plenty of nourishing milk for the foal!

To enable foals to keep up with the herd, a foal's legs are almost as long as it's mother's!

Happy birthday!
Thoroughbred horses all share the same birthday – January 1st! So even if a foal is born in September, it will still be officially a yearling in January!

Playtime!
Foals love to play – and if there ar several in a field together, you will see them running around, rearing together and then sleeping next to mum, exhausted. Then they get up and do it all over again!

Female foals are called fillies. Male foals are colts.

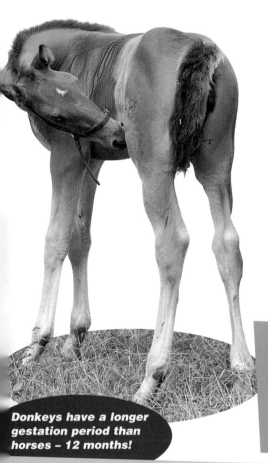

Donkeys have a longer gestation period than horses – 12 months!

Colour matched!

Foals often change their coat colour as they grow – their baby coat may grow out and they become completely different. A lot of foals born chestnut will turn grey!

Grow up!

A newborn foal has to be up and on its feet within an hour of being born. This is because if it were born in the wild, as part of the herd, it would need to be up and able to keep up with the others to avoid being eaten by wolves or big cats. Even though domestic horses and ponies don't have these problems, they still like to be up and suckling as soon as possible.

Something different!

Donkeys and horses can breed together – the gestation period is half-way between the two, and the foal will be either a mule (a donkey sire and a pony dam) or a hinny (a pony sire and a donkey dam). You can even get donkeys crossed with zebras and horses and these will be zedonkeys, or zorses! Offspring of two species are called *hybrids*.

Check out this cute Somalian Wild Ass foal!

10 horsy things
(when you're not riding!)

1 Draw your fave pony

Sounds easy, but it can be very difficult when you get down to it. See whether you can remember all his markings, and the length of his mane and tail. Compare it to the real thing when you go to the stables.

4 Explore the horsy world-wide-web

From the comfort of your armchair you can access masses of info about horses – not to mention keeping up with all things horsy on www.ponymag.com. See you there!

2 Watch a horsy DVD

Choose from instructional (with your fave celeb riders), or the thrill of a competition like Badminton or the World Equestrian Games (exciting!), or even a great horsy story like Black Beauty (get your hankies out). It's a cool way to spend an evening when the weather is bad and the nights are dark.

3 Start a riding journal

Keeping a note of your horsy achievements and lessons is a great way to plot your progress. It's fun, too. Include photographs of your fave pony, or ponies you ride, and look back after a year to see how you've improved!

5 Decide your horsy ambitions

Take a moment to plot your horsy life. Do you want to learn to jump, or ride on the beach, or enter a show? How about writing a horsy story, or exploring how you can work with horses, or even plan for the day when you have your own pony? Horsy dreams are free, but when you start writing them down, you can begin to plan how to make them come true!

to do

You can't ride all the time (wouldn't that be bliss!) but you can still do horsy stuff when you're away from your fave pony – we'll prove it!

6 Hold a model pony show

These are fab fun! Get all your mates to enter their models, persuade your mum or sister to judge and enjoy the show! Decide which classes to have, give your models and extra-special groom, and see who comes out champ.

7 Play a horsy game

Look out for fab games you can play on your computer. Lots of them allow you to choose your horse, groom it, tack it up and go for a ride. You might be able to enter a competition, too. It's almost like the real thing!

8 Design a dream pony

Get together with your horsy mates to design your own dream ponies. They can be any breed and any age. They can be showjumpers, dressage horses, eventers – anything you like! Take it a stage further and decide all the fabulous things you're all going to do with your perfect ponies. You can even send them to PONY Mag to feature in our imaginary pony section!

9 Make a pony scrapbook

You know all those gorgeous pictures of horses and ponies you want to look at again and again? Well, stick them in a scrapbook, and you can! Keeping a pony scrapbook is fun and inexpensive – and it's something you can do in those spare minutes which crop up from time-to-time.

10 Read a horsy book

Get lost in someone's else's life. Reading a pony story can transport you to another world. Get to the library and read, read, read!

And if you're still bored, don't forget to write to PONY Magazine with your drawings, photographs and letters!

Have fun!

Jorja's journal

Since I got my wonderful piebald mare, Jigsaw, I've had a great time with my friend Molly and her pony Star, as well as Matt and his pony, CP. I'm so glad I've got more room to write to you all, because the most exciting thing happened to Jiggy and me in the holidays; we went on a treasure hunt!

Saturday

It's treasure hunt day! Connie, the owner of the riding school, posted a time sheet up on the notice board, and Molly and I were due to start at 11 o'clock. Apparently, everyone sets off in 10-minute intervals, in pairs. We didn't know whether we had to collect things as we rode along, or follow clues, so I'm a bit nervous. I don't think I'm very good at solving clues – I never guess who did it in TV whodunnits!

Matt paired up with a new girl at the yard called Heather for the hunt. She's got a black cob called Charcoal who's got lots of feather – he looks like a cute mini Shire. Actually, I think it was Heather who paired up with Matt – she's been giving him the eye all week, and although Matt seemed flattered at first, she's getting a bit bossy and I think he's getting fed up with her. That should be good sport!

At 11 o'clock, Connie handed us a sheet of paper and wished us luck, and Molly and I rode out of the yard. Jigsaw was a bit fresh and danced about a bit because the weather has turned nippy, and Star jogged too because he hates Jigsaw being in front. Molly was trying to read the Treasure Hunt sheet, but had trouble because Star was jogging so much. And the sheet was upside down!

"What do we have to do?" I asked, trying out my half-halts to keep Jigsaw under control.

"I don't know yet, I can't let go of the reins to look!" replied Molly. This was a sticky start but Molly did manage to look at the sheet, and it is about solving clues. Oh dear, there go our chances.

"*Next to the gate, find a smelly word meaning chicken,*" Molly read aloud. My mind went blank. Zilch. Zippo. Whatever could that mean?

"We'd better find the gate," suggested Molly. This seemed an excellent idea – but which gate?

There was a gate to the field along the lane, and we paused there. Star started digging up the dirt with his off-fore because he hates standing still, and Jiggy tried to graze. I almost got pulled out of the saddle.

"See any smelly words?" asked Molly. I looked at graffiti on the trees, nothing there. What could the clue mean?

"What's this on the ground?" asked Molly, looking at a manhole cover. "It says FOUL, that's a smelly word meaning chicken."

I felt really stupid. What was Molly on about?

"At least it does when it's spelt F-O-W-L!"

I felt even more stupid. Thank goodness one of us has brains. We wrote it down and then saw Matt and Heather approaching.

"Quick," cried Molly, "We don't want to let them see us, they'll find the word." Molly doesn't like Matt.

"Hi girls, found the first clue?" yelled Matt, annoyingly. I could see Heather's mouth opening and closing, even from a distance, she must have been talking nineteen-to-the-dozen. Poor old Matt.

We followed the directions and sped on to the next clue. "*On to where Peter Smith is in charge. When was T Rikmansworth born?*" read out Molly.

"How do we know? What a daft question." I said.

"Well, the answer must be around here somewhere," said Molly. "Who's Peter Smith and why would he be in charge?" I patted Jigsaw and looked around me. There was a church and a notice board in the churchyard. The Rev Peter Smith, said the board.

"In the church!" I almost screamed. I couldn't believe I had solved a clue. At least, I'd solved half a clue!

"Oh, well done Jorja!" said Molly. "But we can't take the ponies in there."

I dismounted and threw Jiggy's reins at Molly. "Who am I looking for?" I asked. "He must be on a gravestone."

"Ugh, I'm glad you're looking then, graves give me the heebie-jeebies," remarked Molly. And so, of course, as soon as she said that, I got a shiver down my spine and wished I hadn't volunteered so keenly.

"Can you see it? Hurry up!" shouted Molly, who was practically knitting with so many reins to hold.

I ran around looking at names. No T Rikmansworth, where was he? I felt a bit

uncomfortable, it wasn't very respectful, running around people's graves. Finally, I found it –

and it was a very old grave. Good old T Rikmansworth was born in 1879, so I guessed no-one would mind us recording the fact. I ran back to Jigsaw, and Molly wrote the clue down. We were riding away before Matt and Heather came into view – Heather's mouth was still going like a ventriloquist's dummy and Matt looked almost ready to make her join T Rikmansworth. Oh dear. I couldn't help laughing. Poor Matt.

Three clues were really easy after that, so I won't bore you with the details, but the next clue was in the village, by the general store. The village is very quiet, hardly any traffic, so it was quite safe. The clue read as follows: *No ers or buts, but you need to find this er to discover the time of the last collection.* That foxed us. We looked at one another blankly. What did that mean? As we looked around wildly Jigsaw chose that moment to do a huge pile of poo, right outside the general store. I could have died with embarrassment. Why now? Why couldn't she have done it on the bridlepath? I hoped no-one was going to kick up a fuss. A woman with a pram went past and gave me a filthy look. I mean, her baby can't control itself, either, and I can't put a nappy on Jigsaw.

Molly started looking in the shop window, and I looked around to see what else what was around. Only a post box. A post box! I steered Jiggy towards it and saw the initials ER on the box. I had no idea why, but there they were. ER. And the times of the collections, when postmen and women collected the letters.

"It's here!" I screamed. The woman with the pram jumped like she'd been shot, and Molly trotted over.

"Oh, well done *you*!" she yelled, writing down the last collection time – five pm.

"So what's with the ER, then?" I asked, feeling dim again.

"*Elizabeth Regina*," said Molly, matter-of-factly. It means the post box was built in the reign of Queen Elizabeth – our queen. Some old ones have other initials on – GR, for example means in the reign of King George." I decided I needed to

pay more attention at school.

There was no sign of Matt. I wondered briefly whether he'd murdered Heather. Or galloped off and left her. Still, not my problem, I decided.

"Next clue," announced Molly, "*On to the Pheasant Woods, trespassers will be what?*" The Pheasant Woods is where we often rode.

"Prosecuted, obviously," I said. I was feeling quite confident now.

"It can't be that obvious," said Molly. We need to go and look." So we did. And it was a good job we did, because the P had rubbed off and it said rosecuted. So that's what we wrote.

"*Wait by the shelter and discover when the last one goes on Saturday,*" Molly read.

"Bus stop!" I exclaimed. We cantered to the bus stop, and I dismounted, running my finger down the timetable to

discover the time of the last bus on Saturdays. 20.00 hours, it said.

"That's early. Not going to be much help if you fancy a great night out," remarked Molly.

"Not our concern," I answered, hopping about on one leg as Jigsaw decided she'd had enough and spun around so I couldn't get on. In the end, Molly grabbed her bridle and I swung into the saddle, at last!

"*Back to the village,*" read Molly. "*How much is the pine bookcase? Oh, how annoying, we could have done that earlier. We should have read all the clues before we started out.*"

Back to the village we cantered, and Jigsaw took a hold so I overshot the bridlepath to the village. It took several wasted moments to regain control (who am I kidding?) and we trotted briskly back to the village shop to peer at the notice board.

"Pine bookcase," read out Molly, "£35 or near offer. I might get my dad onto that, I could do with a bookcase."

"Behave!" I told her.

"Ahhh, there's Matt and Heather. Quick, look at something else, we don't want to give them any clues," Molly hissed at me.

We turned the ponies and started looking in the village shop window, and then Molly pretended to write something down and we trotted off, hoping we'd put them off the scent.

"*Call this number and find out who lives there!*" said Molly.

I pulled out my mobile, punching in the numbers as Molly called them out. We continued trotting so we put distance between ourselves and Matt. A woman answered the telephone.

"Who lives here?" I asked. Bit rude, really!

"What's the password?" came the reply.

"Molly," I said, "I need a password." Molly scanned the clue sheet.

"Here it is! The password is *Herman*." I repeated this into the telephone and got told that Oliver lived there. So Molly scribbled that down and we inspected the sheet again.

"Last clue," announced Molly. "*You can stay here if you pay, but look for the black word seen from the entrance.*"

We looked at one another blankly.

"Stay here if you pay?"

"Black word...?"

"We're stumped. Last clue, too."

We sat in silence, the ponies nipping playfully at each other.

"There's a B&B in the village. You have to pay to stay there," suggested Molly.

"Brilliant – let's go there now!" Turning the ponies (who were a bit fed up by now) we headed for The Swallows B&B. We could see another pair riding away as we arrived, so we thought we were on the

right track.

"A black word. What means black?" asked Molly.

"Dark, *noir*, night, ebony..." I suggested.

"All good," said Molly, "but I can't see them from here. What black word is visible from here?"

I looked around wildly. "There's the petrol station, the pub, a bus stop... none of them are black."

"How about some house names, anything called Raven House or anything?" Molly asked.

"That's impressive, how did you think of that?"

"It's only impressive if it's right!" exclaimed Molly.

I stared at the petrol station. Nothing. Then the pub, The King's Head, nothing there. Nothing at the bus stop...."

"Oh no, here's Matt and Heather. Quick!" cried Molly. I looked again at the petrol station, just a sign saying Jet... JET! Jet *black*!

"Come on, I've got it!" I screamed, and set Jigsaw off along the lane towards the riding school. Molly followed, demanding to know the answer. I didn't tell her until we were almost at the finish – I was thrilled I'd got it, and Molly was impressed, too.

We handed our completed sheet to Connie and put the ponies away. Giving Jigsaw a handful of treats we had one of our special moments where I give her a cuddle, and she lets me. The treasure hunt had been great, and Molly and I had done better than we thought we would. Matt and Heather came home ages after us, and Heather was still talking. Matt looked like a piece of chewed string, and when I caught up with him, he told me he was never going riding with Heather again. EVER!

"Honestly Jorja, I thought my head was going to explode – and she's not too bright, either. I had to do all the work. What was that last clue, anyway?"

"Not saying. You'll know soon enough!" I said mysteriously.

When everyone had finished, Connie added up all the scores and you'll never guess, Molly and I were third! We weren't as fast as the two teams who beat us, but we had all the clues right, so we were thrilled. And I'm not as dense as I thought I was. I hugged Jigsaw and pinned her rosette on her stable door. She's such a superstar!

Jorja x

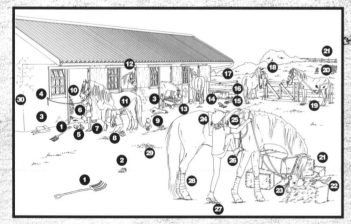

1　Forks lying on yard with prongs upward
2　Cast horseshoe
3　Rugs lying on yard
4　Pony tied directly to ring without string, rope too long
5　Grooming kit lying about on yard
6　Water bucket with handle to the inside of the stable
7　Girl in flip-flops standing under pony, offering tit-bit incorrectly
8　Girl kneeling down, picking out hooves
9　Child sitting behind pony
10　Haynet tied too low
11　Kickbolt not done up
12　Pony wearing headcollar in stable
13　Pony leaning over wheelbarrow, eating feed
14　Pony being led into stable, door not fully open, pony not led in straight

15　Headcollars lying about on yard
16　Dirty water trough
17　Broken fence rail
18　Incorrectly dressed girl turning pony out wrongly – should be facing the gate, and rope should not be wound around her hand. Also, pony has tail bandage o
19　Pony tied directly to gate, rug fastened incorrectly
20　Weeds in field
21　Barbed-wire fencing
22　Scissors and a hoofpick lying about on the haybales
23　Pony eating hay whilst girl trying to mount – reins too long
24　Saddle cloth dirty
25　Girl mounting with chin strap on hat undone
26　Girl mounting from wrong side
27　Girl wearing unsuitable footwear
28　Bandages without padding, and on too loose
29　Dung on yard
30　Bonus point – fire extinguisher and fire notice on yard which were missing before!

How did you do?

Between 1 and 10
Oooh, you need to make sure you're not guilty of any of ou safety issues!

Between 11 and 20
Not bad. You've spotted quite a number of terrible mistakes Just a bit more work needed.

Between 21 and 30
You're good! We can't tell you much about safety on the yard, so well done!

Safety at the yard

How did you get on spotting all the safety errors on pages 66 and 67? **There were loads!**

How did you do?

Here are the answers and solutions to the quizzes on pages 12-13, 32-33, 52-53 and 84-85! Check your score to see how well you did!

Who am I? (pages 12-13)

1. **Exmoor pony**
2. **Icelandic horse**
3. **Poitou donkey**
4. **Ardennais**
5. **Highland pony**
6. **Dartmoor pony**
7. **Hackney**
8. **Suffolk Punch**

On the right tack (pages 32-33)

1. Saddle parts
Pommel, waist, cantle, flap and seat

2. Parts of the bridle
Throatlash, browband, noseband, cheekpiece, headpiece and rein

3. What's wrong with the tack?
a. Saddle too far forward – nasty!
b. Throatlash done up too tightly – strangling pony!
c. Numnah pressing on the withers – this will cause a sore place
d. Cavesson noseband too tight – ouch!
e. Browband too high and squeezing pony's ear.

4. Tack fitting questions

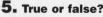

a. A throatlash is correctly fastened when you can fit the width of all four of your fingers on one hand between it and your pony's throat.

b. A correctly-fitted bit should touch the corners of the pony's mouth, just wrinkling the lips.

c. The statement is true, the saddle – and the numnah or saddle cloth – should not touch the pony's backbone, even when a rider is on board.

d. When fastening the girth, use the same tabs on either side of the saddle. Usually, there are three tabs – try to fit your girth to the first and third tab.

e. A drop noseband should never restrict your pony's breathing, so it must be fitted so that you can fit at least three fingers between it and your pony's nostrils.

5. True or false?
a. False
b. True
c. False
d. True
e. False

Quirky quiz (pages 52-53)

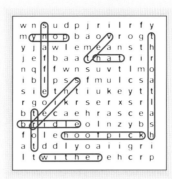

Find the words
Here is the wordsearch solution!

Mystery word
The words you needed to find from the clues were as follows:
1. Cantle
2. Fjord
3. Laminitis
4. Donkey
5. Chestnut
6. Mane
7. Tack
8. Shire
9. Ragwort

The mystery word revealed in the panel should be **Connemara** – Duggie's favourite breed of pony!

Spot the difference
Here is the solution to our teaser!

Match boxes
Can-ter
Sta-ble
Don-key
Hor-ses
Win-ter
Pon-ies
Ene-rgy
Dig-est
Jac-ket

General knowledge
1. Lipizzaner
2. Fibre
3. Przewalskii's Horse
4. Palomino
5. Arabian horses have 17 ribs
6. He is cross, aggressive or in pain
7. Heel to toe
8. Straight ahead
9. Dandy Brush
10. Under the jawbone.

Know your horses! (pages 84-85)

Here's the solution to the quiz – all the words in the wordsearch are the answers! If you're still not sure which answer goes with which question, here's some more help!

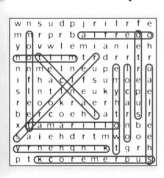

1. Stroller, ridden by Marion Coakes, was the smallest horse ever to win the Hickstead Derby. Only 14.2hh, Stroller also won a silver medal at the Mexico Olympics in 1968!

2. Leslie Law rode Sheer L'Eau to Olympic gold in the Athens Olympics in 2004.

3. Emma Hindle rode Lancet in the 2006 World Equestrian Games.

4. Milton was the first million-pound showjumper! Ridden by John Whitaker, Milton became a household name and the idol of millions!

5.. Ben Maher won the Hickstead Derby in 2005 on Alfredo.

6. Cob of the Year no fewer than six times was the great Super Ted, ridden by Robert Oliver.

7. Mary King's successful eventers included King William, King Boris and King Solomon. So King Henry is the odd-man out, and the answer!

. Ellen Whitaker rode Locarno to finish second to her Uncle John in the Hickstead Derby in 2004.

. Andrew Hoy rode Moonfleet to his first victory at Badminton in 2006.

0. Rolex Grand Slam winner Pippa Funnell rode Supreme Rock at Badminton in 2003.

1. William Fox-Pitt rode Tamarillo in the 2004 Olympic and World Equestrian Games.

2. Two Thyme helped Ruth Edge to victory in the British Open Championship in 2004.

Get close to the special pony in your life with
PONY Magazine...